Measuring Time

TEACHER'S GUIDE

SCIENCE AND TECHNOLOGY FOR CHILDREN®

NATIONAL SCIENCE RESOURCES CENTER
Smithsonian Institution • National Academy of Sciences
Arts and Industries Building, Room 1201
Washington, DC 20560

NSRC

The National Science Resources Center is operated by the Smithsonian Institution and the National Academy of Sciences to improve the teaching of science in the nation's schools. The NSRC collects and disseminates information about exemplary teaching resources, develops and disseminates curriculum materials, and sponsors outreach activities, specifically in the areas of leadership development and technical assistance, to help school districts develop and sustain hands-on science programs.

STC Project Supporters

National Science Foundation
Smithsonian Institution
U.S. Department of Defense
U.S. Department of Education
John D. and Catherine T. MacArthur Foundation
The Dow Chemical Company Foundation
E. I. du Pont de Nemours & Company
Amoco Foundation, Inc.
Hewlett-Packard Company
Smithsonian Institution Educational Outreach Fund
Smithsonian Women's Committee

This project was supported, in part,
by the
National Science Foundation
Opinions expressed are those of the authors
and not necessarily those of the Foundation

ISBN 0-89278-934-4

Published by Carolina Biological Supply Company, 2700 York Road, Burlington, NC 27215.
Call toll free 800-334-5551.

This material is based upon work supported by the National Science Foundation under Grant No. ESI-9252947. Any opinions, findings, and conclusions or recommendations expressed in this material are those of the author(s) and do not necessarily reflect the views of the National Science Foundation.

CB787330109

♲ Printed on recycled paper.

Foreword

Since 1988, the National Science Resources Center (NSRC) has been developing Science and Technology for Children® (STC®), an innovative hands-on science program for children in grades kindergarten through six. The 24 units of the STC program, four for each grade level, are designed to provide all students with stimulating experiences in the life, earth, and physical sciences and technology while simultaneously developing their critical-thinking and problem-solving skills.

The STC units provide children with the opportunity to learn age-appropriate concepts and skills and to acquire scientific attitudes and habits of mind. In the primary grades, children begin their study of science by observing, measuring, and identifying properties. Then they move on through a progression of experiences that culminate in grade six with the design of controlled experiments.

The "Focus-Explore-Reflect-Apply" learning cycle incorporated into the STC units is based on

Alignment of STC® and STC/MS™ Science Curriculum Modules

Grade Level		Life and Earth Sciences		Physical Science and Technology	
STC	K–1	Organisms	Weather	Solids and Liquids	Comparing and Measuring
	2	The Life Cycle of Butterflies	Soils	Changes	Balancing and Weighing
	3	Plant Growth and Development	Rocks and Minerals	Chemical Tests	Sound
	4	Animal Studies	Land and Water	Electric Circuits	Motion and Design
	5	Microworlds	Ecosystems	Food Chemistry	Floating and Sinking
	6	Experiments with Plants	Measuring Time	Magnets and Motors	The Technology of Paper
STC/MS	6–8	Human Body Systems	Catastrophic Events	Properties of Matter	Energy, Machines, and Motion
	6–8	Organisms—From Macro to Micro	Earth in Space	Light	Electrical Energy and Circuit Design

Note: All STC units can be used at one grade level above or below the level indicated on the chart. STC/MS units can also be used at grade 9.

Sequence of Development of
Scientific Reasoning Skills

Scientific Reasoning Skills	Grades					
	1	2	3	4	5	6
Observing, Measuring, and Identifying Properties	◆	◆	◆	◆	◆	◆
Seeking Evidence Recognizing Patterns and Cycles		◆	◆	◆	◆	◆
Identifying Cause and Effect Extending the Senses				◆	◆	◆
Designing and Conducting Controlled Experiments						◆

research findings about children's learning. These findings indicate that knowledge is actively constructed by each learner and that children learn science best in a hands-on experimental environment where they can make their own discoveries. The steps of the learning cycle are as follows:

■ Focus: Explore and clarify the ideas that children already have about the topic.

■ Explore: Enable children to engage in hands-on explorations of the objects, organisms, and science phenomena to be investigated.

■ Reflect: Encourage children to discuss their observations and to reconcile their ideas.

■ Apply: Help children discuss and apply their new ideas in new situations.

The learning cycle in STC units gives students opportunities to develop increased understanding of important scientific concepts and to develop positive attitudes toward science.

The STC units provide teachers with a variety of strategies with which to assess student learning. The STC units also offer teachers opportunities to link the teaching of science with the development of skills in mathematics, language arts, and social studies. In addition, the STC units encourage the use of cooperative learning to help students develop the valuable skill of working together.

In the extensive research and development process used with all STC units, scientists and educators, including experienced elementary school teachers, act as consultants to teacher-developers, who research, trial teach, and write the units. The process begins with the developer researching the unit's content and pedagogy. Then, before writing the unit, the developer trial teaches lessons in public school classrooms in the metropolitan Washington, D.C., area. Once a unit is written, the NSRC evaluates its effectiveness with children by field-testing it nationally in ethnically diverse urban, rural, and suburban public schools. At the field-testing stage, the assessment sections in each unit are also evaluated by the Program Evaluation and Research Group of Lesley College, located in Cambridge, Mass. The final editions of the units reflect the incorporation of teacher and student field-test feedback and of comments on accuracy and soundness from the leading scientists and science educators who serve on the STC Advisory Panel.

The STC project would not have been possible without the generous support of numerous federal agencies, private foundations, and corporations. Supporters include the National Science Foundation, the Smithsonian Institution, the U.S. Department of Defense, the U.S. Department of Education, the John D. and Catherine T. MacArthur Foundation, the Dow Chemical Company Foundation, the Amoco Foundation, Inc., E. I. du Pont de Nemours & Company, the Hewlett-Packard Company, the Smithsonian Institution Educational Outreach Fund, and the Smithsonian Women's Committee.

Acknowledgments

Measuring Time was developed and drafted by Judy Grumbacher, and the final edition was written by David Hartney in collaboration with the STC development and production team. The unit was edited by Kathleen Johnston and Marilyn Fenichel and illustrated by Max-Karl Winkler and Catherine Corder. It was trial taught in the Stuart/Hobson Middle School in Washington, DC, and St. Timothy's School in Garfield Heights, OH.

The technical review of *Measuring Time* was conducted by:

Philip Morrison, Professor of Physics Emeritus, Massachusetts Institute of Technology, Cambridge, MA

Phylis Morrison, Educational Consultant, Cambridge, MA

George Stuart, Archaeologist and Senior Assistant Editor, National Geographic Society, Washington, DC

The unit was nationally field-tested in the following school sites with the cooperation of the individuals listed:

Fresno Unified School District, Fresno, CA
Coordinator: Sheryl Mercier, Science and Health Curriculum Coordinator
Maurine Anderson, Teacher, Ayer Elementary School
Jerry Berman, Teacher, Ericson Elementary School
Karen Wheeler, Teacher, Bethune Elementary School

Christina School District, Wilmington, DE
Coordinator: Ramona Philhower, School Science Coordinator
Peggy Derle, Teacher, Drew/Pyle School
Ann Fleckenstein, Teacher, Drew/Pyle School
Daryl Zarycki, Teacher, Bancroft Elementary School

Fort Bend Independent School District, Sugar Land, TX
Coordinator: Joyce Dutcher, Instructional Coordinator
John Clark, Teacher, Settler's Way Elementary School
Don Johnson, Teacher, Settler's Way Elementary School
Pat Martin, Teacher, Settler's Way Elementary School

The NSRC also would like to thank the following individuals for their contributions to the unit:

Randi Adleberg, Teacher, Fairfax County Public Schools, Fairfax, VA

Anthony Aveni, Professor, Colgate University, Hamilton, NY

Kathleen Baxter, Reference Archivist, National Anthropological Archives, Smithsonian Institution, Washington, DC

JoAnn DeMaria, Teacher, Fairfax County Public Schools, Fairfax, VA

Debby Deal, Educational Consultant, Clifton, VA

John Eklund, Curator, Division of Computers, Information and Society, National Museum of American History, Smithsonian Institution, Washington, DC

Joe Griffith, Director, Hands-On Science Center, National Museum of American History, Smithsonian Institution, Washington, DC

Helen Hengsen, Teacher, Arlington County Public Schools, Arlington, VA

Don Jacobs, Assistant Professor of Physics, The College of Wooster, Wooster, OH

Larry Kirkpatrick, Montana Planetarium Education Project, Bozeman, MT

John Lindner, Assistant Professor of Physics, The College of Wooster, Wooster, OH

George Norton, Technician Specialist, National Museum of American History, Smithsonian Institution, Washington, DC

Dane Penland, Chief, Special Assignments/Photography Branch, Office of Printing and Photographic Services, Smithsonian Institution, Washington, DC

Phil Sadler, Director of Science Education, Harvard-Smithsonian Center for Astrophysics, Cambridge, MA

David Savage, Assistant Principal, Rolling Terrace Elementary School, Montgomery County Public Schools, Rockville, MD

Carlene Stephens, Curator, Division of Engineering and Industry, National Museum of American History, Smithsonian Institution, Washington, DC

Elly Uehling, Teacher, Fairfax County Public Schools, Fairfax, VA

Jane MacLaren Walsh, Museum Specialist, National Museum of Natural History, Smithsonian Institution, Washington, DC

Kay Youngflesh, Museum Specialist, National Museum of American History, Smithsonian Institution, Washington, DC

The librarians and staff of the Central Reference Service, Smithsonian Libraries, Washington, DC

The NSRC is indebted to all of the above individuals, who were instrumental in ensuring the scientific accuracy and pedagogical usefulness of the learning activities in this unit.

Sally Goetz Shuler
Executive Director
National Science Resources Center

STC Advisory Panel

Peter P. Afflerbach, Professor, National Reading Research Center, University of Maryland, College Park, MD

David Babcock, Director, Board of Cooperative Educational Services, Second Supervisory District, Monroe-Orleans Counties, Spencerport, NY

Judi Backman, Math/Science Coordinator, Highline Public Schools, Seattle, WA

Albert V. Baez, President, Vivamos Mejor/USA, Greenbrae, CA

Andrew R. Barron, Professor of Chemistry and Material Science, Department of Chemistry, Rice University, Houston, TX

DeAnna Banks Beane, Project Director, YouthALIVE, Association of Science-Technology Centers, Washington, DC

Audrey Champagne, Professor of Chemistry and Education, and Chair, Educational Theory and Practice, School of Education, State University of New York at Albany, Albany, NY

Sally Crissman, Faculty Member, Lower School, Shady Hill School, Cambridge, MA

Gregory Crosby, National Program Leader, U.S. Department of Agriculture Extension Service/4-H, Washington, DC

JoAnn E. DeMaria, Teacher, Hutchison Elementary School, Herndon, VA

Hubert M. Dyasi, Director, The Workshop Center, City College School of Education (The City University of New York), New York, NY

Timothy H. Goldsmith, Professor of Biology, Yale University, New Haven, CT

Patricia Jacobberger Jellison, Geologist, National Air and Space Museum, Smithsonian Institution, Washington, DC

Patricia Lauber, Author, Weston, CT

John Layman, Professor of Education and Physics, University of Maryland, College Park, MD

Sally Love, Museum Specialist, National Museum of Natural History, Smithsonian Institution, Washington, DC

Phyllis R. Marcuccio, Associate Executive Director for Publications, National Science Teachers Association, Arlington, VA

Lynn Margulis, Professor of Biology, Department of Botany, University of Massachusetts, Amherst, MA

Margo A. Mastropieri, Co-Director, Mainstreaming Handicapped Students in Science Project, Purdue University, West Lafayette, IN

Richard McQueen, Teacher/Learning Manager, Alpha High School, Gresham, OR

Alan Mehler, Professor, Department of Biochemistry and Molecular Science, College of Medicine, Howard University, Washington, DC

Philip Morrison, Professor of Physics Emeritus, Massachusetts Institute of Technology, Cambridge, MA

Phylis Morrison, Educational Consultant, Cambridge, MA

Fran Nankin, Editor, *SuperScience Red*, Scholastic, New York, NY

Harold Pratt, Senior Program Officer, Development of National Science Education Standards Project, National Academy of Sciences, Washington, DC

Wayne E. Ransom, Program Director, Informal Science Education Program, National Science Foundation, Washington, DC

David Reuther, Editor-in-Chief and Senior Vice President, William Morrow Books, New York, NY

Robert Ridky, Associate Professor of Geology, University of Maryland, College Park, MD

F. James Rutherford, Chief Education Officer and Director, Project 2061, American Association for the Advancement of Science, Washington, DC

David Savage, Assistant Principal, Rolling Terrace Elementary School, Montgomery County Public Schools, Rockville, MD

Thomas E. Scruggs, Co-Director, Mainstreaming Handicapped Students in Science Project, Purdue University, West Lafayette, IN

Larry Small, Science/Health Coordinator, Schaumburg School District 54, Schaumburg, IL

Michelle Smith, Publications Director, Office of Elementary and Secondary Education, Smithsonian Institution, Washington, DC

Susan Sprague, Director of Science and Social Studies, Mesa Public Schools, Mesa, AZ

Arthur Sussman, Director, Far West Regional Consortium for Science and Mathematics, Far West Laboratory, San Francisco, CA

Emma Walton, Program Director, Presidential Awards, National Science Foundation, Washington, DC, and Past President, National Science Supervisors Association

Paul H. Williams, Director, Center for Biology Education, and Professor, Department of Plant Pathology, University of Wisconsin, Madison, WI

Science Notebooks in the STC Classroom

Writing is one of the ways that children learn in science. . . . When children explain what they have seen and why they think this occurs in writing, they are forced to clarify their thoughts and organize these ideas in a way that others can understand.

Jenny Feely
"Writing in Science"
in *Science & Language Links*

Every student in an STC classroom should be required to keep a science notebook. Students in grades 3 through 6 can use a loose-leaf binder or a composition book for this purpose; first- and second-graders write directly in their consumable STC Student Notebooks. Students should keep their notebooks with them throughout science class, so that they can add entries daily and review their notes as the unit progresses. Teachers are encouraged to review students' notebook entries periodically to assess their progress in recording the results of their investigations and the growth in their understanding of important concepts.

Why Is a Science Notebook Important?

Science notebooks are important for many reasons. The first reason is that writing is an integral part of the process of learning science. By using notebooks, students model one of the most vital and enduring functions of scientists in all disciplines—recording data. Scientists across the world record their observations and conclusions, as well as comments on their readings and reflections. They rely on their notes when sharing their findings with peers and when preparing the papers in which they share their work with the broader scientific community. The notebooks of famous scientists such as Galileo and Albert Einstein have become part of the world's cultural heritage.

A second reason for maintaining a science notebook is that it provides the student with a ready reference during the unit as well as a resource to consult when reviewing materials at the end of the unit. The notebook is also a means of communicating with other students and with the teacher.

A science notebook encourages the students' creativity. Students are encouraged to draw as well as to write in their notebooks. Keeping a notebook also enhances students' writing skills. It gives them practice in organizing materials and in expressing themselves clearly. At the same time, notebook writing can encourage students to connect science with other areas of the curriculum. Extensions in the STC units, for example, ask students to write poems, stories, or songs, or to do research in related areas such as history and geography.

Another advantage of notebooks is that they get students more involved in science. Students take ownership of their notebooks. As the unit progresses, they have a growing sense of pride in what they have written and learned. Their confidence in their science learning, as well as in their overall knowledge and skills, grows.

Finally, the science notebook offers the teacher a unique means of assessing student progress in science learning. The notebook, ideally begun during the first lesson of the unit and continued to its conclusion, is a tool that can be used to assess the growth in students' understanding of science as well as in their ability to summarize and capture their findings.

Science notebooks are tools for inquiry that allow children to frame questions and seek answers. . . . They are to be used to identify student understanding and misconceptions about science concepts and to inform further practice.

Science Notebook Guidebook
Cambridge Public Schools
Cambridge, Mass.

Incorporating Science Notebooks Into Classroom Activity

Making time for students to write in their notebooks daily can be challenging. With proper planning, however, writing becomes a natural part of the rhythm of the science class.

When to Write

The time at which writing is done depends on the nature of the classroom activity on a given day and on the teacher's choice. What is most important is that students have sufficient time to write, and that they have an opportunity to write in their notebooks daily.

During some inquiries, things may go more smoothly if students suspend their hands-on investigations at certain points, write in their notebooks, and then resume their activity. In other cases, the best time to write is after the inquiry ends. Teachers should allow time for students to share their writing with their peers and the entire class.

Even though students have used their notebooks repeatedly during a lesson, time should always be left at the end of a lesson for students to reflect on what they have learned and to write down any new questions that have arisen.

Notebook Materials

Student notebook materials are diverse. Students may use a bound composition book or a loose-leaf notebook; they can even staple sheets of construction paper around blank or lined paper. Many teachers prefer loose-leaf notebooks because they are more flexible. Folders with pockets and fasteners for three-hole paper also work well because they provide storage space for record sheets, graph paper, and other materials. Other teachers prefer composition books, which deter students from removing or deleting past recordings. Students can glue or tape their record sheets into the composition books.

Notebook Organization

Teachers should make sure that all the students in the class organize their notebooks in the same way. The notebooks should, for example, begin with a table of contents. Students can allow several pages for this at the beginning of the unit. As they begin each lesson, students can then add the title of the lesson to their table of contents. Students should always date their entries and number the pages consecutively throughout the unit. Tabs can help students organize their notebooks and locate specific sections more easily.

Getting Started

Students who have not used science notebooks may need some initial guidance on how to use them most effectively.

You might want to begin by facilitating a brainstorming session designed to increase students' awareness of the importance of maintaining a notebook. Then present some guidelines such as those noted in the previous section.

Tell students that you will be looking at the notebooks often to see how they are doing. At the same time, emphasize that the notebook is primarily for their own benefit. Stress that they should write down not only facts and observations but also questions and ideas they want to further explore.

Help them understand that they should use their notebooks in two major ways. First, they should "take notes" on what they have seen, experienced, and concluded. As they move through the investigation, students should also "make notes"—that is, ask questions and pose comments. Emphasize the importance of always writing clearly and of expressing thoughts in an organized way.

Urge students to use drawings as well as text. They should also be encouraged to design tables and graphs to display findings.

Explain that when you look at the notebooks, you will consider many things. You will look at how complete their entries are. You will also try to determine how much effort they have put into their answers and questions. For a science notebook, this is more important than the "right" answers. Students should think of the information in their notebooks as a rough draft; therefore, you will not assess them on the basis of style, correct spelling, or word usage. The notebooks should, however, be neat and clearly written. The notes that scientists keep must be readable by other scientists, and students' notebooks should meet this same standard.

Organizing the Notebooks

When talking about a good way to organize the notebooks, you might also tell students that the information they write down should be a record of the basic components of their scientific inquiry. These steps are as follows:

- The question that the student wants to answer

- A prediction about how the inquiry will turn out

- The student's plan for the inquiry and the materials that he or she will use

- The student's data and observations (includes words, tables and graphs, and illustrations)

- The student's conclusions
- Next steps or new questions that have arisen from the inquiry

STC lessons generally end with a discussion, during which students share their findings and suggest additional questions to explore. When the discussion ends, you may ask students to return to their notebooks and to summarize, in their own words, the major ideas that have emerged during this discussion. Have students separate these final comments from their previous notes by a horizontal line, which is called the "line of learning."

Keeping a Science Notebook: Student Objectives

After sufficient practice, students who keep science notebooks should be able to do the following:

- Increase their understanding of science concepts.

- Use writing as a process for discovery.

- Improve their ability to organize ideas and information.

- Recognize the connection between thinking and writing.

- Write more freely, more comfortably, and more often.

Adapted from
"Writing for Understanding"
in *Science and Writing Connections*

Reviewing Science Notebooks

Check the students' science notebooks often. Glance at the notebooks during class and collect them periodically for a more detailed review.

You may give feedback to students in many ways. Some teachers prefer to use Post-it Notes™; others write on the notebook page itself; others may prefer to enter their comments in the back of the book. Use a color that is distinguishable from the black or blue that students generally use (green is one idea); it's best not to use red ink. Some teachers ask students to bring their tape recorders to school so they make their comments into the recorder.

Make your feedback positive and constructive. Grade students for the completeness of their work and for their effort. Do not grade ideas as "right" or "wrong." Misspellings or grammatical errors should not be circled or criticized in the notebook. Date and initial all your written comments.

To bring objectivity to the assessment process, some teachers use rubrics. A simple assessment rubric is as follows:

Rubric for Assessing Science Notebooks

STANDARD	SCORE
Date and purpose of inquiry	
Appropriate prediction	
List of materials	
Sequence of procedures	
Diagrams and labels	
Chart or data table as it corresponds to student's results	
Conclusions as they relate to data and answers to the inquiry questions	

3 = Achieved the standard with honors.
2 = Achieved the standard.
1 = Achievement below the standard.
0 = No evidence of achievement.

Conclusion

Student notebooks fill many roles. They promote students' science learning and give students an opportunity to enhance their writing skills. They help students better appreciate the process of scientific inquiry. They help students organize their learning and, by the end of the unit, realize how much they have learned. For teachers, notebooks are a unique means of reviewing student learning.

These guidelines should help you and your students take full advantage of the many benefits that student science notebooks bring to the STC classroom.

Acknowledgment

The NSRC thanks the Cambridge Public Schools and Beckman@Science for providing materials on writing and assessing student science notebooks.

References

Reading

Baker, L., Dreher, M.J., and Guthrie, J. *Engaging Young Readers*. New York: Guilford Publications, Inc. 2000.

Gaskins, I., Guthrie, J., et al. Integrating instruction of science, reading, and writing: Goals, teacher development, and assessment. *Journal of Research in Science Teaching*, 31, 1039-1056. 1994.

Guthrie, J. Educational contexts for engagement in literacy. *The Reading Teacher*, 49, 432-445. 1996.

Guthrie, J., Anderson, E., Alao, S., and Rinehart, J. Influences of concept-oriented reading instruction on strategy use and conceptual learning from text. *The Elementary School Journal*, 99, 343-366. 1999.

Guthrie, J., Cox, K., et al. Principles of integrated instruction for engagement in reading. *Educational Psychology Review*, 10, 177-199. 1998.

Guthrie, J. T., Van Meter, P., Hancock, G.R., et al. Does concept-oriented reading instruction increase strategy use and conceptual learning from text? *Journal of Educational Psychology*, 90, 261-278. 1998.

Palinscar, A.S., and Brown, A.L. Reciprocal teaching of comprehension-fostering and comprehension-monitoring activities. *Cognition and Instruction*, 1(2), 117-175. 1984.

Romance, N., and Vitale, M. A curriculum strategy that expands time for in-depth elementary science instruction by using science-based reading strategies: Effects of a year-long study in grade four. *Journal of Research in Science Teaching*, 29, 545-554. 1992.

Science Notebook Writing

Baxter, G., Bass, K., and Glaser, R. Notebook writing in three fifth-grade science classrooms. *The Elementary School Journal*. 2001.

Beckman@Science. *Introduction to Science Notebooks*. Irvine, Calif.

Cambridge Science Department, Cambridge Public Schools. *Science Notebook Guidebook*. Cambridge, Mass. 2001.

Feely, Jenny. Writing in science. In: Scott, J. *Science & Language Links: Classroom Implications*. Portsmouth, N.H.: Heinemann. 1993.

Freedman, R.L.H. *Science and Writing Connections*. Palo Alto, Calif.: Dale Seymour Publications. 1999.

Keys, C.W. Revitalizing instruction in the scientific genres: Connecting knowledge production with writing to learn in science. *Science Education*, 83, 115-130. 1999.

Klentschy, M., Garrison, L., and Amaral, O.M. (1999). Valle Imperial Project in Science (VIPS) Four-Year Comparison of Student Achievement Data 1995–1999. El Centro, Calif. 1999.

National Council of Teachers of English and The International Reading Association. *Standards for the English Language Arts*. Urbana, Ill.: NCTE. 1996.

Shepardson, D.P., and Britsch, S.J. Children's science journals: Tools for teaching, learning, and assessing. *Science and Children*, 34, 13-7; 46-47. 1997.

Reif, R.J., and Rauch, K. Science in their own words. *Science and Children*, 31, 31-33. 1994.

Daniels, H. *Literature Circles, Voice and Choice in the Student-Centered Classroom*. York, Maine: Stenhouse Publishers. 1994.

Contents

Goals for *Measuring Time*

In this unit, students investigate the history of timekeeping and experiment with various timekeeping devices. From their experiences, they are introduced to the following concepts, skills, and attitudes.

Concepts

■ Time can be measured by observing the natural cycles of the sun and the moon.

■ Shadows cast by the sun can be used to measure and predict the passage of time during a day.

■ The phases of the moon follow a cycle that can be used to measure and predict the passage of time during a month.

■ Mechanical devices can be constructed and used to measure specific intervals of time consistently.

■ The accuracy of mechanical clocks is dependent on their design, the materials from which they are constructed, and their energy source.

Skills

■ Observing and recording information about the natural cycles of the sun and the moon.

■ Learning to plan and conduct experiments in which variables are controlled.

■ Predicting and testing how changing a variable affects the outcome of an experiment.

■ Interpreting test results to draw conclusions about how changing variables affects the outcome of an experiment.

■ Communicating results through writing in notebooks; organizing information in charts, tables, and graphs; and discussion.

■ Reading and researching science materials for more information.

■ Applying previously learned concepts and skills to solve a problem.

Attitudes

■ Developing an interest in exploring and investigating time.

■ Recognizing the importance of repeating tests to validate results.

■ Appreciating the advances people have made in measuring time and explaining natural phenomena.

Unit Overview and Materials List

What is time? This question has intrigued people for centuries. From a philosophical perspective, people have wondered why time only moves forward. From a technological perspective, people have invented a variety of devices designed to keep track of the passage of time.

Measuring Time, a unit on the science and technology of timekeeping, is designed for sixth-graders. It is divided into two sections: "Keeping Time with the Sun and the Moon" and "Investigating Invented Clocks." This organization groups activities involving natural cycles and those involving mechanical methods of keeping track of time. In the first section, students observe the apparent motion of the sun and the recurring cycle of the moon's phases. In the second section, students plan and conduct experiments with some of the principal timekeeping devices developed through the ages, from water clocks to mechanical escapements. Throughout the unit, students read about the history of timekeeping and people's evolving understanding of how to measure time.

In Lesson 1, students participate in a brainstorming session of their ideas about time and timekeeping devices. This is an opportunity for students to share their ideas about time with one another and for the teacher to identify students' interests and to assess their understanding of the subject. Students also estimate the passage of a familiar interval of time—one minute—without using a clock.

Students begin their investigation of natural phenomena used to keep time by constructing their own sun clocks in Lessons 2 and 3. They calibrate these devices by tracing the gnomon's shadow at various times throughout the day. Students also measure the length of the shadow at these times and construct a graph showing the changes.

Lesson 4 presents students with a different type of sun clock—a calendar. Students read about how early civilizations devised calendars based on the counting of sunrises and sunsets and the cycle of the moon's phases. Students also devise their own calendars, which are designed to record the past five days of their own history and to predict the next five days of their future.

In Lessons 5 and 6, students explore the cycle of the moon by making predictions about its phases and then observing them. Many students at this grade level do not understand that the moon's apparent changes involve the relative positions of the observer, the earth, the sun, and the moon. Repeated observation now is important, however, because it provides the experience needed for greater student understanding.

Lesson 7 marks a transition to mechanical means of measuring time. In Lessons 7, 8, and 9, students work on a series of activities in which they construct and regulate sinking water clocks and plan and conduct an experiment with them. Students also read about the history of water clocks.

The cycle of planning and conducting experiments is repeated in Lessons 10, 11, and 12, when students investigate the characteristics of pendulums. In Lessons 13, 14, and 15, students have an opportunity to apply much of what they have learned as they assemble, troubleshoot, and then improve a working clock escapement. The challenge of working with a clock escapement enables students to develop their abilities in solving practical problems.

In Lesson 16, students return to the question of how to estimate the duration of one minute, first considered in Lesson 1. Here, they apply what they have learned to design and construct devices that will help them measure this interval of time.

As students work on these timekeeping devices, they may encounter difficulties and have questions that are not easily answered. In particular, constructing the escapement mechanism provides students with the opportunity to experience firsthand the challenges that scientists and engineers encounter. Throughout the unit, it is important to encourage students toward further experimentation and research as an effective way to broaden their knowledge.

Materials List

Below is a list of materials needed for the *Measuring Time* unit. Please note that the metric and English equivalent measurements in this list and in the lessons are approximate.

1	*Measuring Time* Teacher's Guide
15	*Measuring Time* Student Activity Books
15	cardboard pieces, 10 cm (4″) square
15	plastic bottles with lids, 500 ml (16 oz)
15	plastic bags (to hold 500 ml bottle)
15	metric tape measures, 100 cm long
1	roll of braided nylon casting line, 12-lb test, 50 m (55 yd) long
45	plastic clothespins
60	large washers, 4 cm (1½″) diameter
60	brass washers, 9 mm (⅜″) diameter
16	D-cell batteries
8	flashlights
5	medium funnels
5	bead-tubes (no bead)
5	bead-tubes (orange), 3-mm (⅛″) hole
5	bead-tubes (green), 2-mm (1/12″) hole
15	bead-tubes (yellow), 4-mm (⅙″) hole
15	plastic flex tanks, 4 liters (1 gal)
15	square bases
30	posts, 4.5 cm (1¾″) long
15	end caps, 3.8 cm (1½″) diameter
60	bearings, 5 × 3.8 cm (2 × 1½″)
75	rods, 7.5 cm (3″) long
30	rods, 14 cm (5⅝″) long
45	bushings, 3.8 cm (1½″) diameter
15	rods, 12 cm (4¾″) long
30	rods, 18 cm (7⅛″) long
45	wheels, 5 cm (2″) diameter

15	wooden dowels, 1 cm × 60 cm (⅜ × 24″)
15	C-clamps, 7.5 cm (3″)
1	roll of aluminum foil
1	clock with a sweep second hand
8	sponges
3	buckets
1	roll of waxed paper
8	white plastic beads, 18 mm (¾″) diameter
8	rubber bands, no. 16
30	jumbo paper clips
1	roll of adding machine paper
30	sheets of card stock, 22 cm × 28 cm (8½ × 11″)
8	toothpicks
5	small funnels
15	large funnels
*	Metric rulers
*	Science notebooks
*	Markers
*	Masking tape
*	Calculators
*	Glue or paste
*	Calendar
*	Newsprint

*Note: These items are not included in the kit but are commonly available in most schools or can be brought from home.

Teaching *Measuring Time*

The following information on unit structure, teaching strategies, materials, and assessment will help you give students the guidance they need to make the most of their hands-on experiences with this unit.

Unit Structure

How Lessons Are Organized in the Teacher's Guide: Each lesson in the *Measuring Time* Teacher's Guide provides you with a brief overview, lesson objectives, key background information, materials list, advance preparation instructions, step-by-step procedures, and helpful management tips. Many of the lessons have recommended guidelines for assessment. Lessons also frequently indicate opportunities for curriculum integration. Look for the following icons that highlight extension ideas for math, reading, writing, oral presentations, art, and social studies.

Please note that all record sheets, blackline masters, student instructions, and reading selections may be copied and used in conjunction with the teaching of this unit. For purposes of classroom use only, you may make an overhead transparency of a specific page or item in the Teacher's Guide or Student Activity Book.

Student Activity Book: The *Measuring Time* Student Activity Book accompanies the Teacher's Guide. Written specifically for students, this activity book contains simple instructions and illustrations to help students understand how to conduct the activities in this unit. The Student Activity Book also will help students follow along with you as you guide each lesson, and it will provide guidance for students who may miss a lesson (or who do not immediately grasp certain activities or concepts). In addition to previewing each lesson in the Teacher's Guide, you may find it helpful to preview the accompanying lesson in the Student Activity Book.

Lessons in the Student Activity Book are divided into the following sections, paralleling the Teacher's Guide:

- **Think and Wonder** sketches for students a general picture of the ideas and activities of the lesson described in the **Overview and Objectives** section of the Teacher's Guide

- **Materials** lists the materials students and their partners or teammates will be using

- **Find Out for Yourself** flows in tandem with the steps in the **Procedure** section of the Teacher's Guide and briefly and simply walks students through the lesson's activities

- **Ideas to Explore,** which frequently echoes the **Extensions** section in the Teacher's Guide, gives students additional activities to try out or ideas to think about

Teaching Strategies

Classroom Discussion: Class discussions, effectively led by the teacher, are important vehicles for science learning. Research shows that the way questions are asked, as well as the time allowed for responses, can contribute to the quality of the discussion.

When you ask questions, think about what you want to achieve in the ensuing discussion. For example, open-ended questions, for which there is no one right answer, will encourage students to give creative and thoughtful answers. You can use other types of questions to encourage students to see specific relationships and contrasts or to help them summarize and draw conclusions. It is good practice to mix these questions. It also is good practice always to give students "wait time" to answer; this will encourage broader participation and more thoughtful answers. You will want to monitor responses, looking for additional situations that invite students to formulate hypotheses, make generalizations, and explain how they arrived at a conclusion.

Brainstorming: Brainstorming is a whole-class exercise in which students contribute their thoughts about a particular idea or problem. When used to introduce a new science topic, it can be a stimulating and productive exercise. It also is a useful and efficient way for the teacher to find out what students know and think about a topic. As students learn the rules for brainstorming, they will become more and more adept in their participation.

To begin a brainstorming session, define for students the topics about which they will share ideas. Tell students the following rules:

- Accept all ideas without judgment.

- Do not criticize or make unnecessary comments about the contributions of others.

- Try to connect your ideas to the ideas of others.

Cooperative Learning Groups: One of the best ways to teach hands-on science is to arrange students in small groups. Materials and procedures for many lessons in *Measuring Time* are based on groups of four. There are several advantages to this organization. It provides a small forum for students to express their ideas and get feedback. It also offers students a chance to learn from one another by sharing ideas, discoveries, and skills. With coaching, students can develop important interpersonal skills that will serve them well in all aspects of life. As students work, they will often find it productive to talk about what they are doing, resulting in a steady hum of conversation. If you or others in the school are accustomed to a quiet room, this new, busy atmosphere may require some adjustment.

Learning Centers: You can give supplemental science materials a permanent home in the classroom in a spot designated as the learning center. Students can use the center in a number of ways: as an "on your own" project center, as an observation post, as a trade-book reading nook, or simply as a place to spend unscheduled time when assignments are done. In order to keep interest in the center high, change the learning center or add to it often. Here are a few suggestions of items to include.

- Science trade books on the sun, moon, and stars; timekeeping clocks; and calendars (see the **Bibliography, Appendix B,** for trade book annotations).

- Audiovisual materials on related subjects, such as time travel, psychology of time perception, and time zones.

- Items contributed by students for sharing, such as magazine or newspaper articles, pictures, maps, and models.

Materials

Safety Notes: This unit does not contain anything of a highly toxic nature, but common sense dictates that nothing be put in the mouth. In fact, it is good practice to tell your students that, in science, materials are never tasted. Students may also need to be reminded that looking at the sun, even with sunglasses on, is extremely dangerous and can cause permanent eye damage.

Handling Materials: Some of the activities in this unit involve the distribution and collection of water. In order to conserve water, you will need to establish an effective method of distributing, storing, and collecting water for your classroom. Other classrooms have found buckets with handles to be a good way to smoothly distribute and pour water. Sponges and trays can be used to contain and clean up spills when they occur.

Organization of Materials: To help ensure an orderly progression through the unit, you will need to establish a system for storing and distributing materials. Being prepared is the key to success. Here are a few suggestions.

- Know which activity is scheduled and which materials will be used.

- Familiarize yourself with the materials as soon as possible. Label everything and put on new labels if the old ones become unreadable.

- Organize your students so that they are involved in distributing and returning materials. If you have an existing network of cooperative groups, delegate the responsibility to one member of each group.

- Organize a distribution center and train your students to pick up and return supplies to that area. A cafeteria-style approach works especially well when there are large numbers of items to distribute.

- Look at each lesson ahead of time. Some have specific suggestions for handling materials needed that day.

Additional management tips are provided throughout the unit. Look for the following icon:

Assessment

Philosophy: In the Science and Technology for Children program, assessment is an ongoing, integral part of instruction. Because assessment emerges naturally from the activities in the lessons, students are assessed in the same manner in which they are taught. They may, for example, perform experiments, record their observations, or make oral presentations. Such performance-based assessments permit the examination of processes as well as of products, emphasizing what students know and can do.

The goals for learning in STC units include a number of different science concepts, skills, and attitudes; therefore, a number of different strategies for performance assessment are provided to help you assess and document your students' progress toward the goals. These strategies also will help you report to parents and appraise your own teaching. In addition, the assessments will enable your students to view their own progress, reflect on their learning, and formulate further questions for investigation and research. Figure T-1 summarizes the learning goals for this unit; column one shows where the goals are addressed and column two, where specific assessment strategies are described.

Assessment Strategies: The assessment strategies in STC units fall into three categories: matched pre- and post-unit assessments, embedded assessments, and final assessments.

The first lesson of each STC unit is a *pre-unit assessment* designed to give you information about what the whole class and individual students already know about the unit's topic and what they want to find out. It often includes a brainstorming session during which students share their thoughts about the topic through exploring one or two basic questions. In the *post-unit assessment* following the final lesson, the class revisits the pre-unit assessment questions, giving you two sets of comparable data that indicate students' growth in knowledge and skills.

Throughout a unit, assessments are woven into, or embedded, within lessons. The activities used

as *embedded assessments* are indistinguishable from those in lessons. For embedded assessments, however, the teacher records information about students' learning. Whatever the assessment activity, all are intended to provide an ongoing, detailed profile of students' progress and thinking.

Opportunities for embedded assessments occur at natural points in a unit. In many STC units, the last lesson is also an assessment activity that challenges students to synthesize and apply much that they have encountered in the previous lessons. *Measuring Time* is divided into two sections, and specific guidelines for assessments are presented at appropriate places within each section.

Appendix A contains several final assessments that can be used to document students' understanding after the unit has been completed. In these assessments, students may solve problems through the hands-on application of materials or the interpretation and organization of data. Students may also plan and carry out an experiment. On occasion, an appropriate paper-and-pencil test is included. In addition, **Appendix A** includes a self-assessment that helps students reflect on their learning. When you are selecting final assessments, consider using more than one assessment to give students with different learning styles additional opportunities to express their knowledge and skills.

Documenting Student Performance: In STC units, assessment is based on your recorded observations and students' work products and oral communication. All these documentation methods together will give you a comprehensive picture of each student's growth.

Teachers' *observations and anecdotal notes* often provide the most useful information about students' understanding. Because it is important to document observations used for assessment, teachers frequently keep note cards, journals, or checklists. Many lessons include guidelines to help you focus your observations. Each day, you should try to record your observations of a small group of students. By the end of the unit, you will have numerous observations for every student in your class. The blackline master on pg. 11 provides a format you may want to use or adapt for recording observations.

Work products, which include both what students write and what they make, indicate students' progress toward the goals of the unit. Examine students' work regularly; their written materials should be kept together in their science

continued on pg. 10

Measuring Time: Goals and Assessment Strategies

Concepts	
Goals	**Assessment Strategies**
Time can be measured by observing the natural cycles of the sun and the moon. Lessons 1–6	Lessons 1, 3, 6 ▪ Pre- and post-unit assessments ▪ Record sheets and sketches ▪ Notebook entries
Shadows cast by the sun can be used to measure and predict the passage of time during a day. Lessons 2–3	Lessons 2–3, 6 ▪ Record sheets ▪ Graphs and sketches ▪ Class lists and discussions
The phases of the moon follow a cycle that can be used to measure and predict the passage of time during a month. Lessons 4–6	Lesson 6 ▪ Record sheets ▪ Notebook entries ▪ Class discussions
Mechanical devices can be constructed and used to measure specific intervals of time consistently. Lessons 7–16	Lessons 7–10, 12–14, 16 ▪ Notebook entries ▪ Letters to families
The accuracy of mechanical clocks is dependent on their design, the materials from which they are constructed, and their energy source. Lessons 8–9, 14–16	Lessons 8–9, 14, 16 ▪ Notebook entries ▪ Class discussions ▪ Student self-assessment

Skills	
Goals	**Assessment Strategies**
Observing and recording information about the natural cycles of the sun and the moon. 　　Lessons 2–6	Lessons 2–3, 6 • Notebook entries • Record sheets • Graphs and sketches
Learning to plan and conduct experiments in which variables are controlled. 　　Lessons 7–16	Lessons 7, 9–10, 12–16 • Experiment planning sheets • Record sheets • Notebook entries
Predicting and testing how changing a variable affects the outcome of an experiment. 　　Lessons 7–16	Lessons 8–10, 12–16 • Experiment planning sheets • Graphs and data tables • Notebook entries
Interpreting test results to draw conclusions about how changing variables affects the outcome of an experiment. 　　Lessons 7–16	Lessons 9–10, 12–15 • Notebook entries • Letters to families • Class discussions
Communicating results through writing in notebooks; organizing information with charts, tables, and graphs; and discussion. 　　Lessons 2–16	Lessons 2–3, 6–9, 12–16 • Notebook entries • Class discussions • Record sheets, charts, data tables, graphs • Letters to families
Reading and researching science materials for more information. 　　Lessons 2–5, 7, 12, 14	Lessons 2–3, 7, 12, 14 • Notebook entries • Class lists and discussions • Oral and written reports
Applying previously learned concepts and skills to solve a problem. 　　Lessons 9, 11, 13–16	Lessons 9, 13–16 • Notebook entries • Planning sheets • Class discussions

Attitudes	
Goals	**Assessment Strategies**
Developing an interest and enthusiasm toward exploring and investigating time. 　　Lessons 1–16	Lessons 1, 6, 16, Appendix A • Pre- and post-unit assessments • Class discussions • Notebook entries • Student self-assessment
Recognizing the importance of repeating tests to validate results. 　　Lessons 6–7	Lessons 7, 9, 13–16 • Notebook entries • Record sheets • Student self-assessment
Appreciating the advances people have made in measuring time and explaining natural phenomena. 　　Lessons 1–16	Lessons 6, 15–16 • Class lists and discussions • Notebook entries • Student self-assessment

continued from pg. 7

notebooks to document learning over the course of the unit. When students refer back to their work from previous lessons, they can reflect on their learning.

A variety of materials are produced during a unit. Record sheets, written observations, drawings, graphs, tables, and charts are an important part of all STC units. They provide evidence of each student's ability to collect, record, and process information. Students' science notebooks or journals are another type of work product. Often a rich source of information for assessment, notebooks reveal how students have organized their data and what their thoughts, ideas, and questions have been over time. In some cases, students do not write or draw well enough for their products to be used for assessment purposes, but their experiences in trying to express themselves on paper are nonetheless beneficial. Other work products might include models, posters, and written research reports.

Oral communication—what students say formally and informally in class and in individual sessions with you—is a particularly useful way to learn what students know. Ongoing records of class and small-group discussions should be a part of your documentation of students' learning.

Interviews with your students can be used both to explore their thoughts and to diagnose their needs; patterns in students' thinking often surface, for example, when carefully formulated questions stimulate students to explain their reasoning or the steps they used in a process. The questions that students themselves ask also can be a valuable source of information about their understanding. Individual and group presentations can give you insights about the meanings your students have assigned to procedures and concepts and about their confidence in their learning; in fact, a student's verbal description of a chart, experiment, or graph is frequently more useful for assessment than the product or results. Questions posed by other students following presentations provide yet another opportunity for you to gather information.

Glossary

The glossary for this unit is provided as an additional resource for both teachers and students. The definitions are *not* unit specific and are intended to apply across the STC curriculum. The definitions are provided to facilitate discussion and may serve to enhance other unit activities. *Under no circumstances should students be required to memorize the terms or definitions presented in the glossary.*

Blackline Master
Measuring Time: Observations of Student Performance

STUDENT'S NAME:

Concepts	Observations

Concepts

- Time can be measured by observing the natural cycles of the sun and the moon.

- Shadows cast by the sun can be used to measure and predict the passage of time during a day.

- The phases of the moon follow a cycle that can be used to measure and predict the passage of time during a month.

- Mechanical devices can be constructed and used to measure specific intervals of time consistently.

- The accuracy of mechanical clocks is dependent on their design, the materials from which they are constructed, and their energy source.

Skills

- Observing and recording information about the natural cycles of the sun and the moon.

- Learning to plan and conduct experiments in which variables are controlled.

- Predicting and testing how changing a variable affects the outcome of an experiment.

- Interpreting test results to draw conclusions about how changing variables affects the outcome of an experiment.

- Communicating results through writing in notebooks; organizing information in charts, tables, and graphs; and discussion.

- Reading and researching science materials for more information.

- Applying previously learned concepts and skills to solve a problem.

Section I: Keeping Time with the Sun and the Moon

<table>
<tr><td>

LESSON 1

</td><td>

Before Clocks

</td></tr>
</table>

Overview and Objectives

This first lesson serves as a pre-unit assessment of students' thinking about time. Through a brainstorming session, students discuss and record their ideas about time, and by estimating the duration of a minute, they experience the challenge of actually measuring time. Throughout the unit, students will be exploring different ways to keep track of the passage of time.

- Students brainstorm their ideas and questions about time.

- Students investigate their sense of time by estimating the duration of one minute.

Background

Students have a wide variety of questions about time, from the feasibility of time travel to the origin of time zones to the workings of a clock. To help students get their questions out into the open, and to give you an idea of their thoughts, ideas, and interests, this lesson begins with a brainstorming session. This open exchange of ideas will help you assess what they already know about time. It also will provide you with information to compare to an identical exercise at the end of the unit (see **Post-Unit Assessment**). Figure 1-1 is a list of possible student questions about time.

During the brainstorming session, students are asked to consider how the school day would be different without clocks or calendars. The point of this question is to help students see the need for timekeeping methods. Then they are asked to think of ways to keep track of time without using clocks.

Next, students are challenged to estimate the passage of a minute without using a clock. Students will develop a variety of methods for making this prediction, such as counting, singing songs, guessing, counting heartbeats, and tapping their feet, among other things. Students will compare these strategies for measuring time with those they work on in later lessons.

Materials

For each student
   1 science notebook

For every two students
   1 *Measuring Time* Student Activity Book

For the class
   1 clock with a sweep second hand
      Several sheets of newsprint and marker(s)

Figure 1-1

*Possible
student
questions
about time*

QUESTIONS WE HAVE ABOUT TIME

Why don't 100 minutes = 1 hour?

Why don't 12 hours = 1 day?

Why aren't days shorter?

How can you tell time by the sun?

How can the world run on the same schedule as the clock?

How come time zones are different in different places?

Why do we need time?

Why was time invented?

How come the sky gets pink at sundown?

Preparation

1. Prepare several sheets of newsprint with the headings "What We Know about Measuring Time" and "Questions We Have about Measuring Time" for the class brainstorming session. If necessary, review the suggestions for brainstorming listed in **Teaching *Measuring Time*** on pg. 6.

2. Arrange the classroom so that you are the only one who can see a clock or watch with a sweep second hand.

3. Decide which pairs of students will work together in this lesson.

4. Review this lesson as it is presented in the Student Activity Book. Decide when in this lesson you want to distribute the books to students.

Procedure

1. Ask students to imagine how their school day would be different if clocks and calendars didn't exist. Make a list of their ideas. Students' responses are likely to include some of the following:

   ■ We'd all miss the bus.

   ■ No one will know if you're late.

   ■ I would not know when to get up.

   ■ Lunchtime will never come.

   ■ We'll all stay at school until it gets dark.

2. Ask students to record in their science notebooks their ideas about the following question: How do you think you would tell time if you didn't have a clock or watch?

   Explain to students that they will use their notebook entries to compare what they think now with the ideas they have later in the unit. Remind them to put the date on the notebook page each time they make an entry.

3. Discuss with students the ideas they have about time and timekeeping devices, such as clocks. Ask students to help you make lists on the "What We Know about Measuring Time" and the "Questions We Have about Measuring Time" sheets you have prepared.

   Note: Students will find it useful to refer to these lists throughout the unit as they explore and discover answers to some of their own questions. Also, encourage students to add new ideas and questions to the lists. Use a different color of ink to distinguish new ideas from the original list.

4. Ask students to estimate the duration of a minute. Tell them that you would like them to try measuring time without using a clock or watch.

5. Pair students, and designate one partner as the "predictor" and the other as the "recorder."

6. Show all the students the hand signals you will use to communicate the time. You may want to use a palm down for "early" (before one minute), a thumb up for "on time" (within three to five seconds of one minute), and a palm up (with a shrug) for "after" (later than one minute).

   Note: Be aware that the recorders might be tempted to become coaches. Encourage them to observe only.

7. Tell students that you will signal the beginning of the minute-long interval with a wave of your hand. Ask the predictors to put their heads on their desks and cover their eyes. Ask them to raise their hands when they think a minute has passed.

   Ask the recorders to watch for your signals and to record whether their partners' predictions are early, nearly on time, or late.

8. Tally on the chalkboard the number of predictions that were early, on time (within three to five seconds), and late. Then have students switch roles so that everyone has an opportunity to be a predictor.

9. Again, tally the number of predictions that were early, on time, and late.

Figure 1-2

*Class
brainstorming
session*

10. Discuss with students the strategies that they used to estimate a minute. Questions such as the following may help get the discussion started:

■ What were some of the ways you tried to make your estimate accurate?

■ How do you think you could improve your estimate?

11. Repeat the predict-and-record tests, encouraging students to try a new strategy to improve their estimates. Again, tally the predictions.

Final Activities

1. Discuss with the class how the results of later trials compare with the first trial. Were the estimates improved by using new strategies? Would any of their strategies be a practical way to keep track of time for longer than one minute?

2. Ask students to describe in their notebooks the methods they used to estimate the duration of a minute. Remind students to record the date of their entries. Explain that they will be constructing devices to measure the duration of a minute and other time intervals in later lessons.

Figure 1-3

Teacher tallying predictions on the chalkboard

Extensions

1. Ask students to begin a time diary. They could start their diaries by recording the number of times in a 24-hour period that they look at a clock or watch or ask someone what time it is. Then have them record the time and the reason they needed to know the time. For example, did they want to know when school was over or how long they would have to wait until dinner?

   Encourage students to compare their time diaries with other students' diaries. Are there certain times of the day when many students are especially curious about the time?

2. Ask students to help create a class list entitled "Things We Can Do in One Minute." Below are some examples.

   ■ Turkessa's heart beats 60 times.

   ■ Javon can count to 90.

   ■ Marcia can sing "Happy Birthday" 4 times.

   Challenge students to devise questions for each other, such as "How many times will Turkessa's heart beat in three and a half minutes?" Or, "Can Javon count to 30 before Marcia finishes singing 'Happy Birthday' once?" Questions such as these will encourage students to compare a variety of strategies for estimating the duration of one minute.

Figure 1-4

A variety of ways
to estimate
a minute

Assessment

Teaching *Measuring Time*, on pg. 5, includes a detailed discussion about the assessment of students' learning. The specific goals and related assessments for this unit are summarized in Figure T-1 on pgs. 8 and 9. Lesson 1, Lesson 16, and the post-unit assessment following Lesson 16 include activities designed to serve as pre- and post-unit assessments of students' ideas.

1. In Step 2 of the **Procedure** section, students respond in their notebooks to the question, "How do you think you would tell time if you didn't have a clock or watch?" These responses are the first half of a pre- and post-unit assessment. They also can provide some information about the ideas your students already have about the concept of timekeeping. Look at the number of ideas your students have and at whether or not they seem wedded to only one way of keeping track of time.

2. The brainstorming session conducted in this lesson also can be used as the first half of a pre- and post-unit assessment. The class lists generated during this session provide information about how and what students think about time at this point in the unit. This information can help you tailor your instruction to best meet the needs of your students.

Making a Record of Shadows

Overview and Objectives

In Lesson 1, students estimated the length of a minute and experienced the challenge of marking the passage of time. This activity sets the stage for investigations of natural timekeeping phenomena, such as the cycles of the sun and moon. People have used the sun as a timekeeper for thousands of years. In this lesson, students record the sun's changing position in the sky throughout the day by marking the location of shadows cast by a device called a gnomon. Observations made in this lesson provide a shadow pattern that will be used as a sun clock in Lesson 3.

- Students observe the change in shadows cast by the sun.

- Students record the changes they observe by marking the position of shadows at various times throughout the day.

Note: The sun must be out in order to do the activities in Lessons 2 and 3. If the sun isn't out, skip ahead to Lesson 4 and come back to Lessons 2 and 3 when it is sunny.

Background

Sun clocks, or sundials, work by making use of the way that sunlight casts shadows of objects. From most perspectives in the Northern Hemisphere during most of the year, the sun appears to move in a southerly arc across the sky from east to west as the earth rotates. This causes the direction and length of an object's shadow to change throughout the day, following a northerly arc from west to east. By marking the position of a shadow at various times of day, it becomes possible to keep track of the passage of time.

Many sun clocks use what is called a **gnomon**, or shadow-caster, to cast a shadow on a dial. In this lesson, students use a vertical plastic rod as a gnomon to cast a shadow on a piece of paper. Then they trace the shadow at different times of day to record the changes in shadow length and position.

When students make their observations, it will be helpful for them to know which directions are east and west. This will help students orient their sun clocks the same way each time they use them. Familiar landmarks, such as distant buildings or trees, can be used to align the paper consistently. Placing the gnomon in the middle of the southern edge of the paper allows for a range of morning and afternoon shadows to be recorded on the paper.

Figure 2-1

Sun shadows in most of the Northern Hemisphere move from west to east

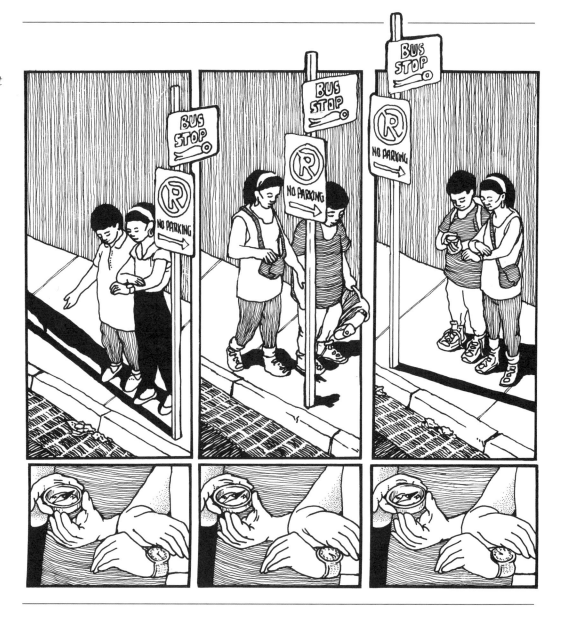

Although sun clocks were developed to divide days into smaller units of time, many ancient cultures developed highly accurate systems for following the sun's motion over greater time periods. Observations of the sun and other celestial objects were used to predict the seasons and eclipses. **Appendix E** provides additional background information on some of the most famous ancient observatories—Stonehenge, the Wyoming Medicine Wheel, and the Mayan pyramids.

Materials

For each student

1   science notebook
1   sheet of 22 cm × 28 cm (8½″ × 11″) card stock
1   7.5-cm (3″) rod (or one pencil*)
1   wheel, 5 cm (2″) diameter
1   pencil (to use as a gnomon in the spring and summer months)
1   ruler

Figure 2-2

Making a simple sun clock

* A longer gnomon, such as a pencil, may be needed in the spring and summer because the sun is farther north in the sky at that time of year and casts shorter shadows. The shadows will be particularly short at latitudes nearer the equator. The 7.5-cm rods, or an even shorter substitute, can be used in the fall, winter, and early spring.

Preparation

1. If at all possible, arrange to begin this lesson in the morning. That way, students can construct the sun clock and record the changes in shadows at each hour throughout the day.

   If you work with students for only one period each day, recording the shadows may require some special arrangements. The following suggestions may be helpful:

   ■ Ask other teachers for their cooperation in permitting students to take a few minutes to trace the shadows each hour.

   ■ Arrange for students to calibrate their sun clocks at home on a weekend or holiday.

   ■ Encourage students to cooperate with each other to gather the information they need. Ask students who can calibrate the sun clocks in the morning to share data with those who can calibrate the clocks in the afternoon.

2. In order for students to calibrate their sun clocks, they need to be in a sunny place. A room with large windows and a southern exposure works best, but any room that receives direct sunlight at least part of the day can be used. Or, you can have students work on this activity outside. (If students do work outside, they will have to have access to a watch.)

3. Determine which directions are east and west and display this information in the classroom.

Safety Reminder: Caution students never to look directly at the sun, even when wearing sunglasses. The sun's energy can cause eye damage in just a few seconds.

Procedure

1. Ask students to discuss their ideas about how the sun could be used to mark the passage of time. Their ideas are likely to range from "watch the shadows move" to "use a sundial" to "count sunsets." Then explain to students that in this lesson they will be constructing a sun clock.

2. Encourage students to share any questions they would like to try to answer about sun clocks. Add these questions to the list of questions begun in Lesson 1 on the sheet entitled "Questions We Have about Measuring Time."

3. Distribute the materials. Ask students to use the directions on pg. 11 of the Student Activity Book to construct a sun clock. These directions are found on pg. 26 of the Teacher's Guide.

4. Ask students to predict where they think the shadow will appear in one hour. What will the shadow do? Have students record their predictions in their notebooks along with sketches and the reasons for their predictions.

5. Ask students to share their predictions and their reasons for them with the rest of the class. This discussion will provide you with information about students' ideas about the sun, shadows, and time. Most students believe that the shadows will change, but they will provide a wide variety of reasons for this belief. Some examples of their ideas are listed below.

   ■ The sun rises higher up so that shadows get shorter.

   ■ Every day the earth rotates and it makes the shadow move.

   ■ The shadow will point over here, because the sun is moving.

   ■ I've seen my shadow in the afternoon, and it goes that way.

Final Activities

1. Arrange for students to calibrate their sun clocks by tracing the shadows at regular intervals throughout the day. Ideally, this could be done each hour.

2. Ask students to read "Sun Clocks" on pg. 10 of the Student Activity Book (pg. 27 of the Teacher's Guide). The following questions may help students focus on the reading.

   ■ Why do you think sun clocks are used less frequently than they once were?

   ■ Why do you think sun clocks become less accurate when they are moved from place to place?

3. After students have had a chance to calibrate their sun clocks, ask them to review their predictions. In their notebooks have them compare their predictions with their observations.

Note: The students will be using their sun clocks in the next lesson.

Extensions

1. Observe the motion of shadows cast by tall buildings or other structures. Have students mark the corner of a "tall" shadow with a piece of chalk, then wait two minutes and mark it again. Depending on the height of the object casting the shadow, the shadow may have moved several inches in just a short period of time. Repeat this process several times to mark the shadow's motion.

2. When students trace the gnomon's shadows on their sun clocks, have them record the length of their own shadow, too. As long as the measurements are taken at the same time of day, the ratio of the student's height to the length of his or her shadow will always be the same as the ratio of the height of the gnomon to the length of its shadow. For example, if a student is 120 cm (47″) tall, his or her shadow will be 80 cm (32″) long. The gnomon is 9 cm (3½″) high and casts a shadow that is 6 cm (2⅓″) long. In both cases, the ratio is 3:2.

   Student's height/student's shadow = 120 cm/80 cm

   Gnomon's height/gnomon's shadow = 9 cm/6 cm

   Then challenge students to compare the object height/shadow length ratios for a variety of objects.

3. Ask students to make up their own saying about time and the sun to put on a sundial.

Assessment

1. In Step 5 of the **Procedure** section, students predict what they think will happen after they trace the first shadow. Look at these notebook entries for evidence that students have had experience making observations of shadows or shadow motion.

   ■ Do students already know what will happen or are they merely guessing?

   ■ Are the reasons that students give for their predictions based on their experiences or on something that they have been told?

2. Look at students' notebook entries. Is there evidence that students have compared their observations with their predictions? Help students understand that making and testing predictions is a useful process for learning new things and not a matter of getting right and wrong answers.

Student Instructions for Building a Sun Clock

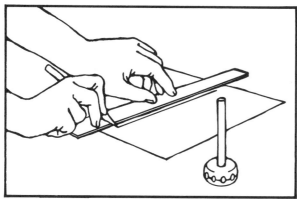

1. Use a pencil and a ruler to draw a straight line across the middle of the paper.

2. Trace the outline of the plastic wheel in the middle of one edge of the paper. This will be the southern edge of your sun clock. Ask for help if you are uncertain which direction is south.

3. Find a familiar landmark that will help you remember which way is south. Draw a small arrow on your sundial that points to this landmark. This will help you put your sundial in the same place and point it in the same direction each time you use it.

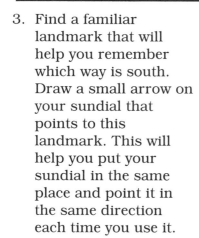

4. Trace the shadow that the gnomon makes on the paper. Label it with the time of day.

   Repeat this step at regular intervals (as determined by someone's clock or watch) throughout the day.

Reading Selection

Sun Clocks

Sundial mounted vertically on a wall

Sun clocks, or sundials, have been around for centuries. The Egyptians used them more than 3,000 years ago, and they remained very popular throughout the world until the Industrial Revolution, a little more than 100 years ago. Sundials are still used in this country today, but people don't rely on them the way they once did.

Sundials come in all shapes and sizes, and they are made of a variety of different materials.

Some are as large and crude as slabs of stone; others are as small and delicate as a watch. But no matter how different they look, sun clocks all work essentially the same way—by the sun casting the shadow of a gnomon on a dial.

Simple sun clocks require adjustment throughout the year. That's because the path the sun appears to take across the sky changes with the seasons. For people in the Northern Hemisphere, the sun appears to cross higher in the sky each day from approximately December 22 to June 21, and lower in the sky from June 22 to December 21.

Another complication is that a sundial made to work in one place needs to be reset in order to work in another place. So, a sundial can tell time accurately at one latitude (the latitude in Egypt, for example) but not be accurate at a different latitude (such as the latitude in Greece). This is because the angle of the sun's rays is slightly different at different latitudes. You can see the different latitudes of Greece and Egypt on a globe of the earth.

Today sundials are not used as often as modern clocks and watches to tell time. But you can still see them, usually as ornaments in parks and gardens. They are worth looking for. They come in many different designs and often have various inscriptions carved into the dial. Look for sayings such as the following.

"Let others tell of storms and showers, I only mark the sunny hours."

"Use the day well."

"Nobody looks at me when the sun is not there."

"The sun shines for all."

Traditional sundial

LESSON 3

Does the Sun Move?

Overview and Objectives

Through today's activities, students continue to refine their ideas about how the sun can be used to keep track of time. They do this by measuring the length of the shadows that they traced in Lesson 2 and using their measurements to construct a graph of shadow length. To reexamine their ideas about how shadows change, students also use a model to simulate the sun's apparent motion.

■ Students analyze their observations from Lesson 2 and use them to construct a graph.

■ Students shine a flashlight on their sun clocks to produce simulated sun shadows.

■ Students record and discuss observations and questions about sun clocks.

Background

Students constructed their sun clocks in Lesson 2. Now they get an opportunity to investigate some of the clock's characteristics. One investigation involves measuring and graphing the length of the shadows cast at different times of day. The graph will show the pattern of shadows getting shorter and then longer again as the day passes.

Another investigation with the sun clock is to cast shadows with a flashlight used to simulate the sun. Such a model makes it possible for students to observe how shadows of various lengths and in various directions are produced. Students can be encouraged to change the shadows both by moving the flashlight while keeping the sun clock fixed and by moving the sun clock while keeping the flashlight in one position. In this way, they can simulate a day's worth of shadows in a much shorter period of time.

By manipulating this model, students may begin to become aware of how the earth's rotation produces the apparent motion of the sun in the sky. This is a sophisticated notion, however, and students will consider this view at widely varying times in their lives.

If students continue to observe their sun clocks for several weeks, they will discover that the dials need to be redrawn every few weeks if they are to measure time accurately. This is because the sun appears to shift north and south in the sky as the seasons change. *Sundials: Their Theory and Construction*, by Albert Waugh, is a good reference guide to the technical aspects of sundial construction. See the **Bibliography (Appendix B)** on pg. 159 for a description.

Materials

For each student

   1 science notebook
   1 sun clock (from Lesson 2)
   1 copy of **Record Sheet 3-A: Graphing Shadow Length**
   1 copy of **Record Sheet 3-B: Sun Clock Time**

For every two students

   1 metric tape measure

For every four students

   1 flashlight
   2 D-cell batteries
   1 rubber band
   1 piece of waxed paper, 10 cm (4″) square

Preparation

1. Make one copy of **Record Sheets 3-A** and **3-B** for each student.

2. Cut one 10-cm (4″) square of waxed paper for each team of four students.

3. Decide how you will group students into teams of four. These teams will be working together to recreate shadows on the sun clock with a flashlight.

Procedure

1. Ask students to describe what they discovered about sun shadows and sun clocks in Lesson 2. Make a list of their observations. Figure 3-1 shows a list of past students' observations.

2. Explain to students that shadow length is one observation that they can measure directly. One way they can display their observations is by constructing a broken-line graph.

3. Ask students to measure the length of the shadows they have traced and to graph the shadow lengths for each time of day on **Record Sheet 3-A**. Can they use the graph to estimate lengths for times of day when they were unable to measure the shadows?

   A completed graph may look something like Figure 3-2, depending on which time of year the data is collected and at what latitude. (In fall and winter the shadows will be longer than in the spring and summer, unless a different-sized gnomon is substituted.)

4. Arrange students in teams of four. Ask them to use their graphs and sun clocks to discuss questions such as the following:

   ■ When was the shadow the shortest? When was it the longest?

   ■ How does the length of the shadow compare to the length of the gnomon?

   ■ In what ways did the shadows change during the day?

   ■ How could you predict the length and location of a shadow for a particular time?

5. Ask the teams to report briefly on their discussions so that the entire class can share information.

Figure 3-1

*Students' ideas
about sun shadows
and sun clocks*

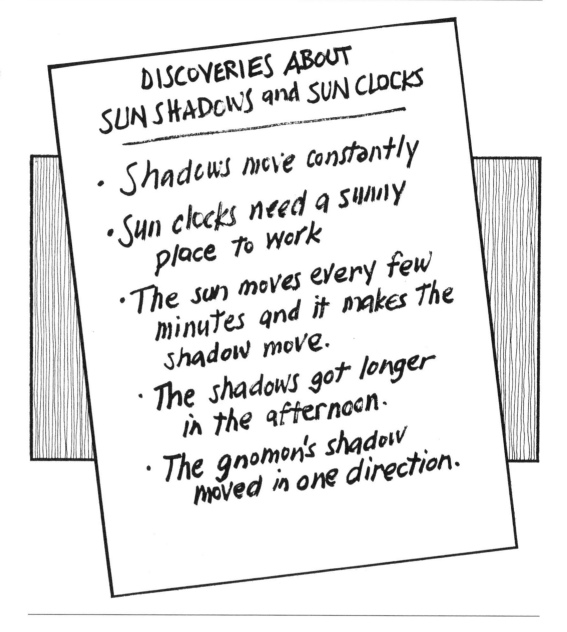

DISCOVERIES ABOUT
SUN SHADOWS and SUN CLOCKS

- Shadows move constantly
- Sun clocks need a sunny place to work
- The sun moves every few minutes and it makes the shadow move.
- The shadows got longer in the afternoon.
- The gnomon's shadow moved in one direction.

6. Challenge the teams of four students to use a flashlight to reproduce the shadows that the sun made on their sun clocks. To reduce glare, have students cover the front of the flashlight with a piece of waxed paper attached by a rubber band.

7. Distribute the materials. Ask students to attempt to make the shadows change in two ways:

   ■ By moving the flashlight while keeping the sun clock still

   ■ By moving the sun clock while keeping the flashlight in one place

   Students probably will find it useful to dim the lights in the classroom and to move the flashlights at least 1 m (approx. 3 ft) from the gnomon in order to produce sharp shadows.

Figure 3-2

*Sample graph showing the length of shadows
at different times during the day*

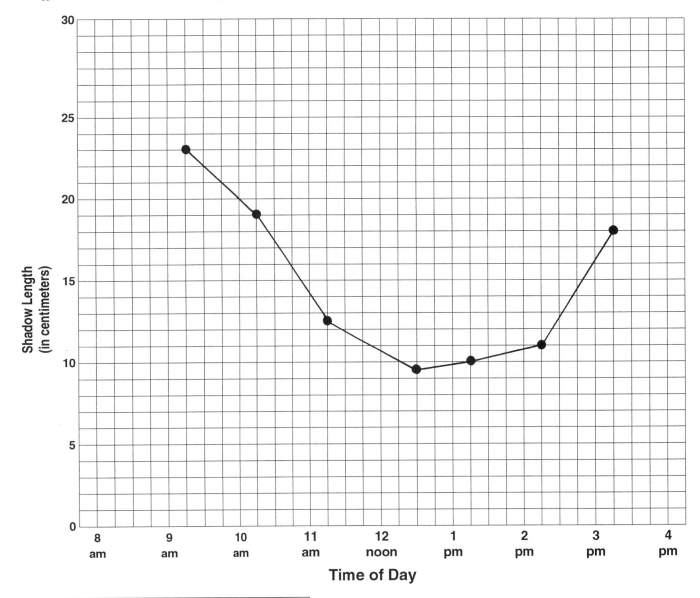

Time of Day	Shadow Length (centimeters)
9:15 a.m.	23
10:15 a.m.	19
11:15 a.m.	12.5
12:30 p.m.	9.5
1:15 p.m.	10
2:15 p.m.	11
3:15 p.m.	18

Location: Parking lot of St. Timothy's School, Garfield Heights, Ohio, October 15, 1992

Figure 3-3

Simulating sun shadows

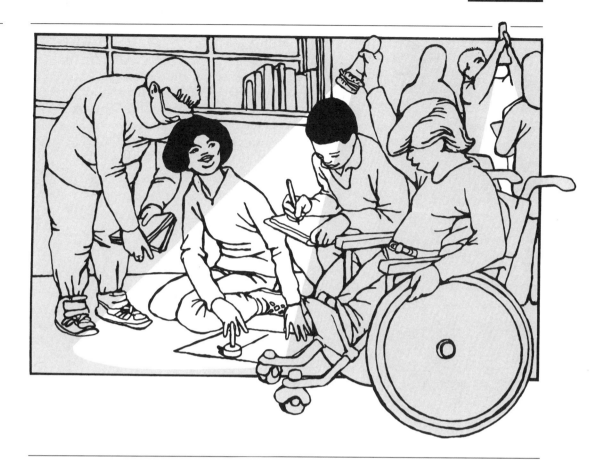

Final Activities

1. Ask students to record in their notebooks the experiences they have had with sun clocks. Ask them to write and draw to explain what they have done. Encourage them to include any questions they have as a result of their experiences.

2. Have students read "The Sun-Shadow Knows," on pg. 16 in the Student Activity Book (pg. 38 of the Teacher's Guide). Help students focus on the reading by asking them questions such as the following:

   ■ How can you tell whether it is a dangerous time of day for a sunburn?

   ■ What do you think makes certain times of day safer to be in the sun?

3. Ask students to complete the questions on **Record Sheet 3-B: Sun Clock Time**. Suggest that they use their sun clocks, graphs, and notebook entries as references.

Extensions

1. The ratio of height to shadow length is the same for all objects that are measured at the same time. This makes it possible to determine the height of tall objects by comparing their shadows with the shadows of other objects of known height. For example, in the situation shown in Figure 3-4, the child's height is 1.5 m (approx. 5 ft), and his shadow is 2.25 m (approx. 7½ ft) long. Since the street lamp's shadow is 9 m (approx. 30 ft) long, it follows that the street lamp is four times taller than the child, or 6 m tall (approx. 20 ft). Challenge students to find the height of the street lamp—and other tall objects—by measuring the length of shadows.

Figure 3-4

Shadows can be used to find the heights of tall objects

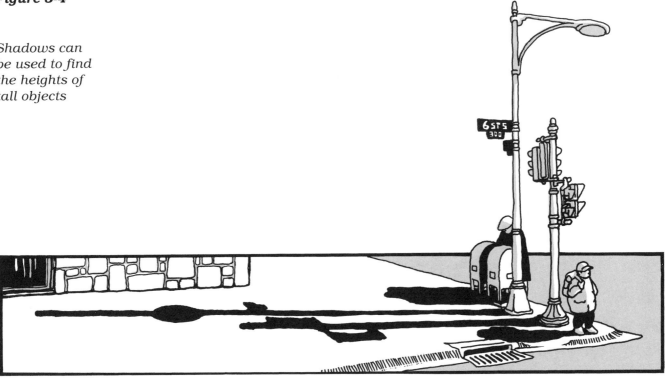

Object	Length of Shadow (meters)	Height of Object (meters)
Student	2.25	1.5
Traffic light	6	?
Street lamp	9	?

2. Encourage students to make and investigate other types of sun clocks—either ones they design or that others design. *Sundials and Timedials*, by Gerald Jenkins and Magdalen Bear, and *This Book is about Time*, by Marilyn Burns, are two books that contain patterns and directions for making sun clocks. See the **Bibliography (Appendix B)** for more information.

3. Invite students to read *Sun Calendar*, by Una Jacobs, which is referenced in the **Bibliography (Appendix B)**. It contains information about plants that bloom at different times throughout the day.

4. Ask students to investigate the gods in Greek and Roman mythology, particularly the sun god, Apollo.

Assessment

1. Your students' measurements and graphs of shadow length provide evidence of their ability to use a ruler and to graph data. Look for students who need additional practice with these important skills.

2. Students' responses to the questions on **Record Sheet 3-B** show the extent to which they understand two important points:

   ■ The sun's shadows change in a predictable pattern.

   ■ The sun's shadows can be used to keep track of the passage of time.

   In reviewing **Record Sheet 3-B**, you may discover that your students need more time working with the sun clock.

Reading Selection

The Sun-Shadow Knows

An easy-to-use rule for safety in the sun that works anywhere in any season, according to the National Cancer Institute (NCI): When your shadow is shorter than you are tall, the sun can burn, so cover up.

The shadow method, developed by meteorologist-astronomer Leith Holloway of time, your shadow length on a level surface is equal to your height.

Sun safety rules based on time of day may not be adequate because the relationship between clock time and the sun's distance from the zenith varies considerably with changes in season and geographic location, NCI says.

Chevy Chase, Maryland, is based on the principle that the closer the sun comes to being directly overhead, the stronger are its burning ultraviolet (UV) rays. The atmosphere, and especially its ozone layer, absorbs most of the dangerous UV radiation from the sun, but the small amount that does reach the ground can cause sunburn.

As the sun sinks in the sky in the afternoon, its increasingly slanted rays must pass through more and more air and ozone. By the time the sun reaches the point between the zenith (overhead point) and the horizon, enough of the harmful UV rays are blocked for the sunlight to be relatively safe. At that

The shadow method eliminates these problems by allowing you to determine whether the sun's angle is in the danger zone. Use your foot as a ruler for pacing off and estimating shadow length. In general, about six personal foot-lengths are equal to your height.

Users of the shadow method, or any other sun-safety guideline, should be cautioned that the effects of harmful UV exposure are cumulative and that safe limits vary widely by individual.

(Reprinted with permission from *The Washington Post.*)

Record Sheet 3-A

Name: _____

Date: _____

Graphing Shadow Length

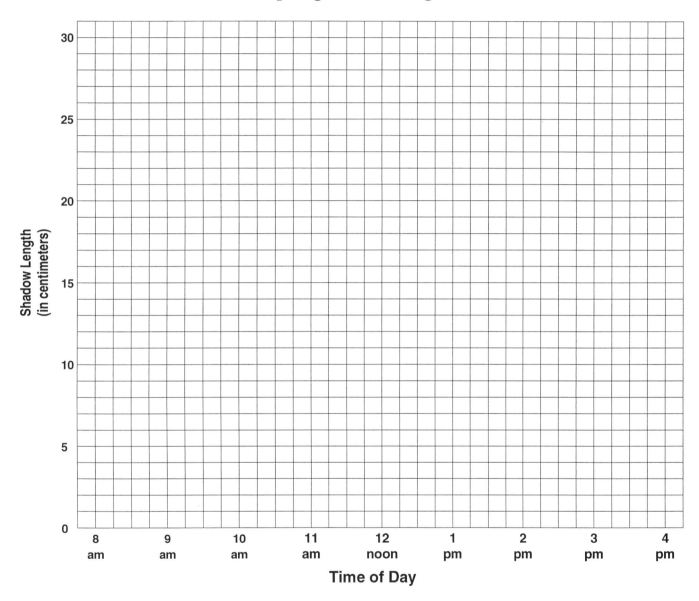

Record Sheet 3-B

Name: _____

Date: _____

Sun Clock Time

1. Not all the times on this sun clock have been marked. Please write them in.

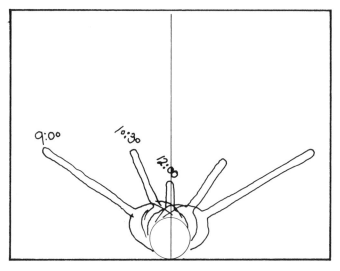

2. Where will the shadow be at 9:30, 2:30, and 3:15?

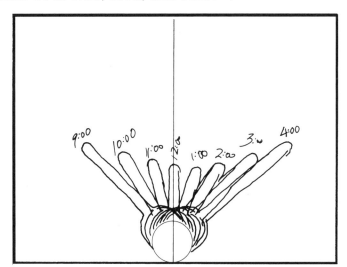

3. At what times do you think shadows as long as these would be made? Write down what you think. What facts about the sun and shadows can you use to help you?

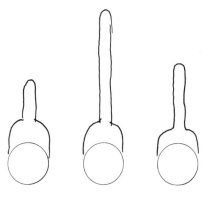

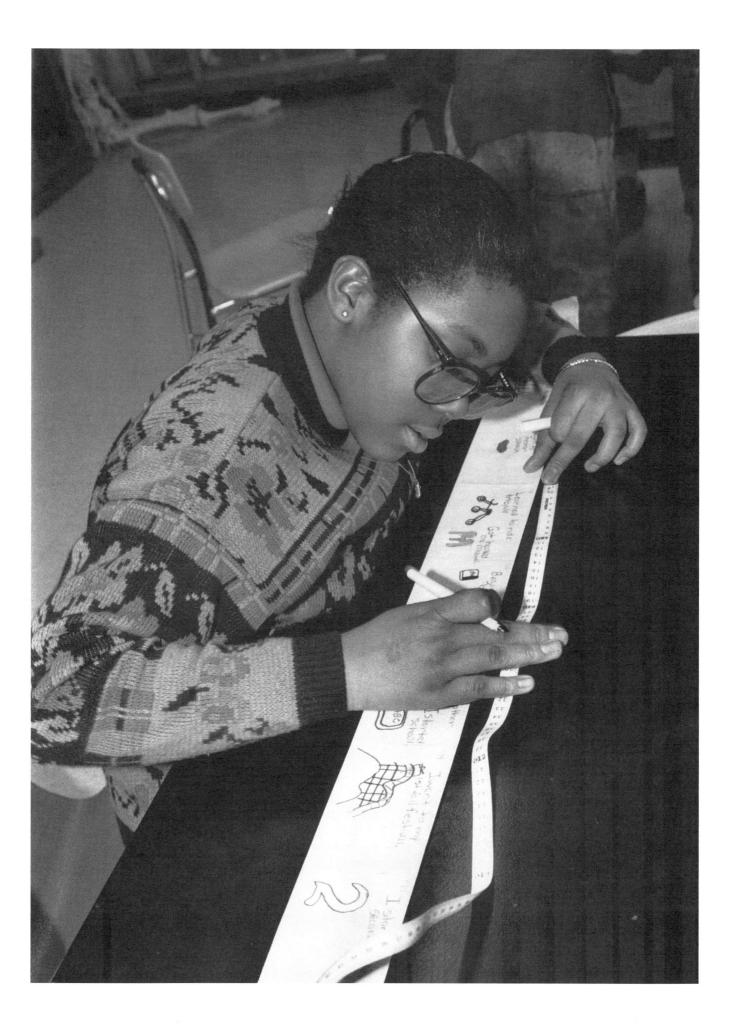

Counting Days: Devising a Calendar

Overview and Objectives

The calendar was one of the first devices people developed to keep track of time. Calendars enabled them to count the passage of days and to predict the return of seasons. To develop a better understanding of the value of calendars, students devise their own personal calendars that record the events of their recent past (the past week) and predict the events of their immediate future. After reading about calendars used by other cultures, students observe that although all calendars count days, they can take many different forms.

■ Students read about calendars used by other cultures.

■ Students design and construct their own calendars.

■ Students discuss different methods they have used to measure time.

Background

Counting days, as calendars do, is a fundamental way to measure the passage of time. Calendars can even be thought of as a very basic form of sun clock—a sunrise followed by a sunset equals one day. Long before human beings understood that the earth rotated on its axis to cause day and night, people around the world used the counting of days for remembering the past ("how long ago") and planning the future ("when it will happen").

Our current calendar, with its 7-day weeks, leap years, and 28-, 30-, and 31-day months, is a result of centuries of changes. Parts of previous calendar systems from many different cultures and geographic locations have been combined for a complex variety of reasons to produce the system we now use. In this lesson, students read about some of the interesting history of calendars.

Materials

For each student
   1   science notebook
   1   strip of adding machine paper, 60 cm (24") long

For every two students
   1   metric tape measure, 100 cm

For the class
   1   calendar

Preparation

1. Cut one 60-cm (24″) strip of adding machine paper for each student.

2. Display a calendar for the class.

3. Decide which students will work together in teams of four during this lesson.

Procedure

1. Ask students to describe the observations they made of sun shadows and sun clocks in Lessons 2 and 3. Explain to students that calendars are a kind of sun clock, too, because counting days—sunrises and sunsets—is a way to keep track of the passage of time.

2. Direct students' attention to the calendar you have displayed. Ask students to work in teams of four to discuss and list what they know about how our calendar system is used to keep track of time. Questions such as the following may help promote the discussion:

   ■ What are some ways that our calendar system is used to keep track of time?

   ■ Why do you think calendars were invented?

   Students probably will focus on the number of days in a week, the seasons, their birthdays, and on many other aspects of calendars. Ask them to record their ideas in their notebooks.

   Note: Most students know quite a bit about our calendar system. This activity provides an opportunity to assess whether some students need additional information and to provide it if necessary.

3. Ask each team to share what they discussed with the class.

4. Ask students to read "Early Calendars," on pg. 19 in the Student Activity Book (pg. 46 of the Teacher's Guide) to learn about the ways several other cultures have kept track of the passage of time. To help students focus on the reading, ask questions such as the following:

   ■ What are some ways that other cultures have organized their calendar systems?

   ■ What do you think are some of the advantages or disadvantages of our current calendar compared with earlier calendars?

5. Challenge students to design a calendar on a strip of paper that records the events of the past five days and predicts the future—the events of the next five days. Ask them to show the passage of days and to use drawings to record the events. Figure 4-1 shows several student-designed calendars.

6. Distribute the strips of paper to students.

Final Activities

1. Ask students to take turns describing their calendars to the rest of the class. Suggest that they explain their calendars and the reasons for their predictions for the future.

2. Review with students the methods they have used to keep track of time. Observing sun shadows and counting sunrises and sunsets to make calendars are two ways they have explored. Then ask students to share their ideas of other ways to record the passage of time.

3. Explain that observing the moon is another way to tell time and that it too has been used by people in the past. In the next lesson, students will begin observing changes in the moon's appearance.

Figure 4-1

Student-designed
calendars

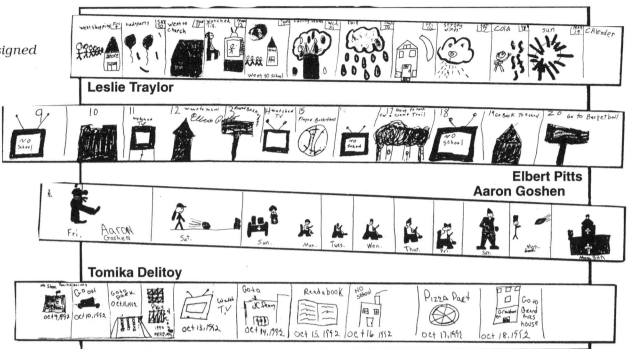

Leslie Traylor

Elbert Pitts
Aaron Goshen

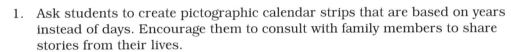

Tomika Delitoy

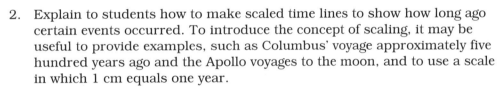

Extensions

1. Ask students to create pictographic calendar strips that are based on years instead of days. Encourage them to consult with family members to share stories from their lives.

2. Explain to students how to make scaled time lines to show how long ago certain events occurred. To introduce the concept of scaling, it may be useful to provide examples, such as Columbus' voyage approximately five hundred years ago and the Apollo voyages to the moon, and to use a scale in which 1 cm equals one year.

3. Using the daily newspaper, have students record the time of the sunrise and the sunset over a long period of time so that they can compare the length of days throughout the year. Write the information on a card each day and post the cards around the room so the change in daylight hours can be observed easily.

4. Ask students to keep track of the passage of days without using a paper and a pencil. Challenge them to devise a three-dimensional calendar, such as a notched stick or pebbles in a jar.

Reading Selection

Early Calendars

Native American elder explaining calendar stick to children

Long ago, early civilizations devised calendar systems that were very different from the calendar we use today. Each of the early systems was unique to the culture it served, but all the calendars had something in common: they were used as a way to keep track of the occurrence of natural events, such as the changes in the seasons and the phases of the moon. And they were used to predict when these changes would happen again in the future. All of these early calendars relied on counting days—sunrises and sunsets—as a way to keep track of the passage of time.

The Early Egyptians

In ancient Egypt, the annual flooding of the Nile River was a very important event because it enriched the soil of the valley so the crops would grow. Because it was important to know when the river would flood and when it would recede, the ancient Egyptians divided their year into three seasons: Inundation (or flooding), Cultivation, and Harvest. Each of these seasons was four months long, with each month consisting of 30 days. This system had five "leftover" days each year. Those days were considered unlucky for some reason, and not a good time to be born.

The Early Chinese

The ancient Chinese did not have just one calendar system; they had many, which is understandable, given the great number of different cultures in China. The earliest Chinese calendar systems were based on the changing phases of the moon. The calendar months were made up of 29 and 30 days, alternately.

Later, the Chinese switched to a calendar based on the position of the sun in the sky (much like our current calendar). Under this sun-based system, the Chinese devised a number of different ways to divide the year. One such calendar had 24 periods, with 15 days each. This calendar was based on the activities of farmers and the weather at various times of the year.

Native Americans

In the Americas, Native Americans kept track of long periods of time by observing the moon's phases. And they named their moon months according to events they observed in their surroundings. For example, the Kiowa people, who lived in what is now the south-central United States, called the beginning of spring Little-bud moon, when trees began budding. In late autumn, they named a month Little-moon-of-deer-antlers-dropping-off.

Similarly, the Inuit people, living in what is now the state of Alaska, began their year with a moon called It-is-cold-the-people-are-fishing. When the weather became warmer,

there was a moon known as The-seals-are-shedding-their-coats.

Pima calendar stick

Calendar Sticks and Calendar Robes

To keep track of historical events, some Native Americans painted or scraped symbols on animal skins and on sticks of wood. These symbols, or pictographs, depicted what had happened and when.

The figures at the lower left are some pictographs made by a member of the Kiowa tribe. The small spotted person on the left represents a winter when smallpox killed many members of the tribe. The stars above the next person recall a spectacular meteor shower. The last pictograph on the right represents a major victory in battle over a rival tribe. The Kiowa commonly used arrows to depict battles.

The Pima people, who still live in what is now the southwestern United States, carved symbols into wooden sticks to help them remember their personal history and the history of the tribe. They would make notches in the sticks to indicate moons and years, and they would use the sticks when telling stories to remind themselves of what came next.

Other Civilizations

Other civilizations also looked at the patterns of night and day, the changing seasons, and the changing appearance of the moon and used them to keep track of the passage of time and to predict future events. The Akan of Africa developed a calendar based on their farming activities. The Mayans, Incas, Babylonians, Aztecs, Greeks, and Romans all devised a variety of calendar systems.

Kiowa pictographs

Predicting the Phases of the Moon

Overview and Objectives

Like sun shadows and calendars, the changing phases of the moon mark a cycle that can be used to keep track of the passage of time. In fact, the word "month" is derived from an ancient word for moon. In this lesson, students begin observing the changing phases of the moon. Using their current knowledge of the moon, students record predictions about the sequence of the phases. Throughout the rest of the unit, students will make observations to test their predictions. Over time, students' observations may help them understand the complex phenomenon of the moon's changing phases.

- Students compile lists in their notebooks of things they know about the moon and questions they have about the moon.

- Students record predictions about the sequence of the moon's phases on moon-phase cards.

- Students observe the moon's phases.

Note: If possible, it will be helpful to conduct this lesson when the moon is near its first- or last-quarter phase. During these phases, the moon may be visible during the school day. At last quarter, the moon sets at approximately midday, so it is visible on clear mornings. At first quarter, the moon rises at approximately midday, so it is visible on clear afternoons and evenings. At full moon, the moon rises as the sun sets. Check the newspaper to find out the moon's current phase.

Background

While the moon is certainly safer to observe than the sun, it is often difficult to locate. This is because the moon appears in the sky a little less than one hour later each day. For example, if the moon rose at approximately 3 p.m. today, it will rise a few minutes before 4 p.m. tomorrow. Also, the sky needs to be relatively cloud-free. For these reasons, Lessons 5 and 6 require careful planning—and a little luck.

Students often expect the moon to be visible every day or night at a particular time—perhaps because they observed it once or twice before at that time—or they expect the moon to be visible every time they look at the sky. Some students may conclude that if the moon isn't visible when they look for it, then it must be a new moon.

Despite these challenges, observing the moon's cycle on a regular basis over a long period of time is a valuable educational activity. Discovering the pattern of the moon's phases by direct observation makes a powerful impression on many students.

Figure 5-1

The view from
earth of a crescent
moon at sunset

Students begin their study of the moon by using what they already know about the moon's phase to make preliminary predictions about what the pattern will be for the next 30 days. Moon-phase cards make it possible for students to concentrate on the predicted sequence of phases and to try out and revise a variety of sequences. It may be necessary to remind some students that the purpose of making and testing predictions is to learn something new; sometimes students are overly concerned with "getting the right answer." Making these predictions may help motivate students to look for the moon on successive days and nights. Regular observations may enable students to recognize the cyclic pattern of the moon's phases.

Over the course of the next 30 days, students will be attaching the moon-phase cards to long strips of adding machine paper. It will be helpful to designate a location in the classroom, such as a wall or bulletin board, where students can hang their strips. This will prevent the paper from becoming crumpled in desks and will remind students to continue observing the moon.

Below are some additional suggestions for conducting the moon observation activity:

- It may be helpful to designate a particular time of day for attaching the moon-phase card to the strip.

- Suggest that on cloudy days, students attach a blank piece of paper with the word "cloudy" and the date on it. After 30 days, students can compare the predicted moon-phase for the cloudy days with the pattern before and after the cloudy days. Does the prediction fit the pattern?

- Help students distinguish among different phases by pointing out features to look for. For example, if you are facing south, a last-quarter moon is lighted on the left and appears flat on the right. A first-quarter moon is lighted on the right and appears flat on the left.

Figure 5-2

*Last-quarter
and first-quarter
moon phases*

Materials

For each student
1 science notebook

For every two students
1 set of 30 moon-phase cards
1 strip of adding machine paper, 150 cm (60″) long
1 paper clip
1 bottle of glue or paste

For the class
1 calendar
1 sheet of newsprint and a marker

Preparation

1. Using the blackline masters on pgs. 56 and 57, duplicate one set of moon-phase cards for every two students. Cut the sheets apart into 30 individual cards and clip them together with a paper clip. You may want to enlist student helpers for this task.

2. Cut one strip of adding machine paper for every two students.

3. Research which phase the moon is in tonight so that you can tell your students. Or, ask students to conduct this research on their own. Most newspapers list the phase of the moon and times for moonrise and moonset on the weather page. Current editions of almanacs also contain this information.

4. As in Lesson 4, display a wall calendar in your room. Students may find a calendar useful when they begin recording the dates of their predictions in Step 7 of the **Procedure** section.

Procedure

1. Ask students to retell what they learned from reading "Early Calendars." Then explain that in this lesson they will begin observing and making predictions about the moon, which was an important part of ancient calendars.

2. Ask students to make a list in their notebooks of what they know about the moon. Then compile their ideas on newsprint in a class list entitled "What We Now Believe about the Moon." This list is likely to be quite extensive. And it may contain information that is incorrect. Remind students that they will reexamine this list later on to see what they have learned (see **Appendix A**). Figure 5-3 lists several student responses.

3. Ask students to add any questions they have about the moon to the list of questions about time, which they began in Lesson 1.

4. Display the moon's phase for today or tonight by sketching it on the chalkboard. Ask students whether they observed a similar phase yesterday and if so, when they made the observation. Give students some advice about when and where to observe the moon over the next several days and nights.

5. Arrange students in teams of two and ask them to use the moon phase cards to predict the future. You may want to ask a question such as the following: "How do you think the moon's phase will appear over the next 29 days?" Then distribute the moon-phase cards to each pair of students.

Figure 5-3

*Students' comments
about the moon*

WHAT WE NOW BELIEVE ABOUT
THE MOON

The moon is very bright
The moon has craters
Men have walked on the moon—
Neil Armstrong.
The moon changes shape, some-
times it is only a half moon
It makes it get dark
The moon is out during the day
sometimes.
A half moon is called a quarter
moon
A quarter moon looks like a banana.
There are 12 full moons in a year

6. Challenge students to work together to arrange the cards in the order they think the moon's phases will appear, beginning with the moon's current phase.

7. After students have arranged the cards, ask them to find the card that matches the phase you sketched on the chalkboard. Then have them record today's date in the box provided on the card.

8. Explain that each moon-phase card has a space to record the predicted date and a different space to record the date that the phase was actually observed. Ask students to record the predicted dates of each phase on the remaining moon-phase cards. Then stack the cards in order and clip them back together.

Final Activities

1. Distribute the strips of adding machine paper to each pair of students. Ask them to glue or paste today's moon-phase card near one end of the strip of paper. Explain that this strip will be a record of their observations. They will attach a new moon-phase card each day, after they have observed the moon's phase.

2. Ask students to post their strips in a designated area of the classroom and to keep the remaining moon-phase cards in a safe place, such as their notebooks.

3. Remind students to look for the moon over the next several days. Encourage them to check the newspaper, an almanac, or television weather reports for information about when the moon will rise.

Extensions

1. Encourage students to read "Moon Myths: Why the Moon Waxes and Wanes," on pg. 24 of the Student Activity Book (pg. 55 of the Teacher's Guide).

2. Discuss with students the Mayan calendar, which predicted astronomical events with remarkable accuracy.

3. Ask students to create and illustrate their own myths to explain the waxing and waning of the moon.

Reading Selection

Moon Myths: Why the Moon Waxes and Wanes

What causes the moon's changing phases? For thousands of years, people from all around the world have come up with explanations for this complex phenomenon. These explanations, or myths, have been handed down from generation to generation and are part of our cultural heritage.

Below are two myths about the moon. The first is from the Iroquois Indians of what is now New York State. The second is from the San of the Kalahari Desert in southern Africa.

The Old Iroquois Woman and the Cat

According to Iroquois legend, an old woman was sent to the moon because she was unhappy that she could not tell when the world would come to an end. Her fate then was to spend her days weaving a basket beside a pot of simmering corn. Every month, when the basket is almost finished, the old woman puts it down to stir her pot. From earth, this looks like a full moon. But as the old woman stirs, her cat unravels her work. During this time, the moon wanes until it becomes invisible from earth. Month after month the old woman works, fated to continue her labors until the world comes to an end.

The Sun and the Moon

According to the San, the full moon is a joyous sight, lighting the way for weary travelers. But the sun, fiery and jealous, doesn't want the moon to shine so brightly in the sky. He tries to chase the moon away, but the moon continues to shine in the sky. Enraged, the sun carves bits and pieces off the moon. Little by little, the moon is whittled down until almost nothing is left.

The moon is afraid that she is going to die. She begs the sun to spare at least her backbone. The sun relents, leaving the wounded moon her backbone.

The moon goes into hiding to recover from her injuries. Slowly, she regains her strength. She begins appearing in the night sky again until she becomes full and shines brightly all night long. Seeing this, the sun becomes angry and jealous. Once again, he repeats his monthly assault to diminish the moon's light.

Date predicted | Date observed

Date predicted | Date observed

Date predicted | Date observed

Date predicted | Date observed

Date predicted | Date observed

Date predicted | Date observed

Date predicted | Date observed

Date predicted | Date observed

Date predicted | Date observed

Date predicted | Date observed

Date predicted | Date observed

Date predicted | Date observed

Date predicted | Date observed

Date predicted | Date observed

Date predicted | Date observed

Date predicted   Date observed

Date predicted   Date observed

Date predicted   Date observed

Date predicted   Date observed

Date predicted   Date observed

Date predicted   Date observed

Date predicted   Date observed

Date predicted   Date observed

Date predicted   Date observed

Date predicted   Date observed

Date predicted   Date observed

Date predicted   Date observed

Date predicted   Date observed

Date predicted   Date observed

Date predicted   Date observed

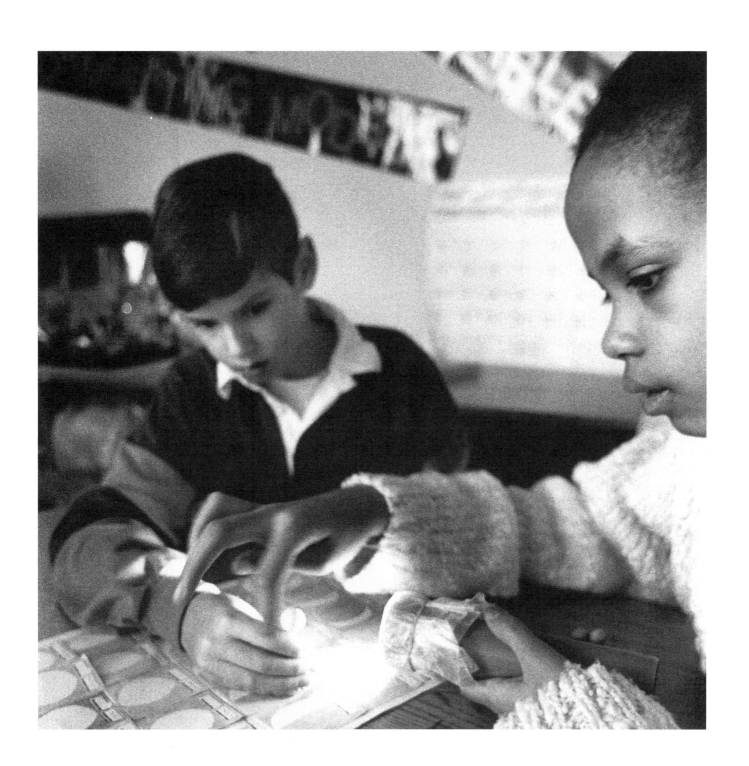

Observing the Phases of the Moon

Overview and Objectives

In this final lesson of the unit's first section, students continue observing the moon to modify their predictions, and they keep ongoing records of their observations. To better understand that the phases follow a familiar, observable, and repeating pattern, students manipulate a model that simulates them. This experience gives students another opportunity to explore the moon's phases. By the end of the month, students will have a better understanding of the moon's month-long cycle.

- Students examine the moon-phase predictions they made in Lesson 5.

- Students manipulate a three-dimensional model to simulate the phases of the moon.

- Students discuss and refine their ideas about the cause of the moon's phases.

Background

Students have many different ideas about what causes the moon's phases. Some students may think that the phases are caused by the earth's shadow; others, by permanently light and dark sides of the moon or even by clouds. These ideas may be based on firmly held beliefs, so they probably will not be changed easily.

Other students may already have ideas that are closer to current scientific explanations of the cause of the moon's phases. They may know that sunlight strikes the moon and is reflected to the earth. They also may know that the changing phases are caused by the changing angle at which we view the moon and that the phase observed depends on the relative positions of the moon, the sun, and the observer on earth. Some students may even consider the changing phases of the moon as a type of natural clock, which in fact they are.

The most productive way for students to come to a genuine understanding of the moon's phases is by observing the moon repeatedly as its appearance and position in the sky change. Using a bead model, like the one introduced in this lesson, can help students better see what phase the moon is in when they actually observe the moon. When held up "next" to the moon on a day when the sun and moon appear together in the sky, the model is in the same phase as the moon (see Figure 6-1).

In addition to using the bead while observing the moon outside, students also use it as part of a simulation they perform in the classroom. By manipulating the relative positions of the bead, a flashlight, and themselves, students will be able to simulate the various phases of the moon—new, crescent, quarter, gibbous, and full. Figure 6-2 shows what these phases look like. This activity is conducted by teams of students so that there is ample opportunity for discussion.

Figure 6-1

Using a bead
to simulate the
moon's phase
when the sun
and the moon
are in the sky
at the same time

Figure 6-2

Five phases
of the moon

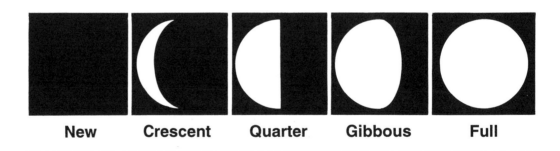

| New | Crescent | Quarter | Gibbous | Full |

One experience shining a flashlight on a plastic bead is not likely to translate immediately into total understanding of the relative positions and complex motions of the earth, the moon, and the sun necessary to produce the moon's phases. But it may motivate students to begin to ask and consider important questions about the moon. Student-generated questions, such as those listed below, can be a springboard for further research.

- How can the moon be out during the day?

- What makes a new moon?

- Why is the moon sometimes up in the morning? In the afternoon?

- How come we never see the other side of the moon?

■ What does it mean that the earth rotates?

■ What is an eclipse of the moon (lunar eclipse)?

■ What is an eclipse of the sun (solar eclipse)?

Before students can fully understand the causes of the moon's phases, even when they observe what happens to a model, they must first recognize that the phases follow a familiar, observable, and repeating pattern. Figure 6-3 shows an illustration of this model. This concept is important for increased understanding of the phases of the moon.

Note: Questions about solar and lunar eclipses often arise naturally out of discussions about the moon's phases. If models are used in connection with these discussions, it is extremely important that accurate scale models be used to simulate eclipses so that observations of the model are not misleading. **Appendix F**, on pg. 175, contains additional information about eclipses.

Figure 6-3

A model for understanding the phases of the moon

Materials

For each student

1   science notebook

For every two students

1   set of moon-phase cards (from Lesson 5)

For every four students

1   white plastic bead, 18 mm (¾") diameter
1   flashlight
1   rubber band
2   D-cell batteries
1   piece of waxed paper, 10 cm (4") square
1   toothpick

Preparation

1. A good time to conduct this lesson is several days after Lesson 5. This will give students an opportunity to observe the moon for themselves and begin to observe the pattern of moon-phase changes.

2. Cut one 10-cm (4") square of waxed paper for each team of students. Cover the flashlight with the waxed paper using a rubber band. This will cut down on the glare of the light and will make it easier for students to concentrate on simulating phases by changing the relative positions of the light, the bead, and the observer.

3. Look in the sky, the newspaper, or an almanac to find out the current phase of the moon.

4. The room in which you teach this lesson needs to be darkened. To test the darkness of the room, try shining the flashlight on one of the beads to see if you can create the different phases shown on the moon-phase cards.

Procedure

1. Ask students to share the moon-phase predictions that they made in Lesson 5 and their subsequent observations of the moon. As mentioned in Step 1 of the **Preparation** section, it will be helpful if students have had an opportunity to observe the moon for several days before beginning this lesson. That way, students will have already recorded some of their observations—by gluing several moon-phase cards onto a strip of paper.

2. Ask students who observed the moon this morning or last night to sketch the current phase of the moon on the chalkboard. Then have all students sketch the current phase in their notebooks. Ask students to work with their partners to find the moon-phase card that represents the current phase.

3. Explain to students that they will be using a flashlight and a plastic bead to make a model of the moon's phases, beginning with the current phase.

4. Arrange students in teams of four, with one student designated as the flashlight holder; another, the bead holder; and two students, the observers/recorders of moon phases. Ask students to rotate these responsibilities so that everyone has a chance at each role.

5. Distribute the materials. Ask students to work with their team to create a situation so that, to the observer, the bead appears to be in the same phase as the current moon phase. Suggest that the bead holder hold the bead up in the air.

6. Ask students to discuss why they think the phase appears different depending on where the observer is located. Remind the recorders to sketch the positions of the light, the bead, and the observer in their notebooks, along with a sketch of the phase that was simulated (see Figure 6-4).

7. After each team member has had an opportunity to simulate and observe the current moon phase, challenge the teams to produce other moon phases. Ask students to simulate full, crescent, and quarter phases. Have them repeat this while keeping the flashlight and the observer fixed, moving only the moon.

8. Have students switch roles until each member of the team has had an opportunity at each role.

Final Activities

1. Ask students to respond to the following question by writing and drawing about their ideas in their notebooks:

    ■ What do you think causes the changing phases of the moon?

2. Have the class share their ideas and ask students to discuss the evidence they have to support their ideas. Then encourage them to continue observing the moon and testing their ideas.

Extensions

1. Set up a learning center about the moon. Include materials from this lesson so that students can continue to try out their ideas. **Appendix D** contains other suggestions.

2. When the sun and moon are in the sky at the same time, have students simulate the moon's phase with the plastic bead (see Figure 6-1). Ask them to explain their observations.

3. Encourage students to make a flipbook that shows the changes in the moon's phases.

Assessment

This lesson is the final lesson of **Section I: Keeping Time with the Sun and the Moon**. It is a natural place to assess students' progress.

Look at students' work products, such as their notebook entries and other products listed in Figure T-1 on pg. 8, for evidence that students have made progress in understanding the observable changes of the sun and moon and how they can be used to keep track of time. You also may find the following questions helpful in assessing your students' progress.

■ Can students predict accurately how a sun shadow will change? Look at their work on **Record Sheets 3-A** and **3-B** for evidence that they recognize this pattern.

■ Do students understand that the moon passes through predictable phases? Examine their sequence charts, notebook entries, and sketches.

■ Do students have ideas about what causes the moon's phase to change? Review their responses to this question, asked in Step 1 of the **Final Activities** section (Lesson 6).

■ What evidence have students displayed that they understand the challenge of measuring the passage of time?

Figure 6-4

Student sketches of the flashlight, bead, and observer

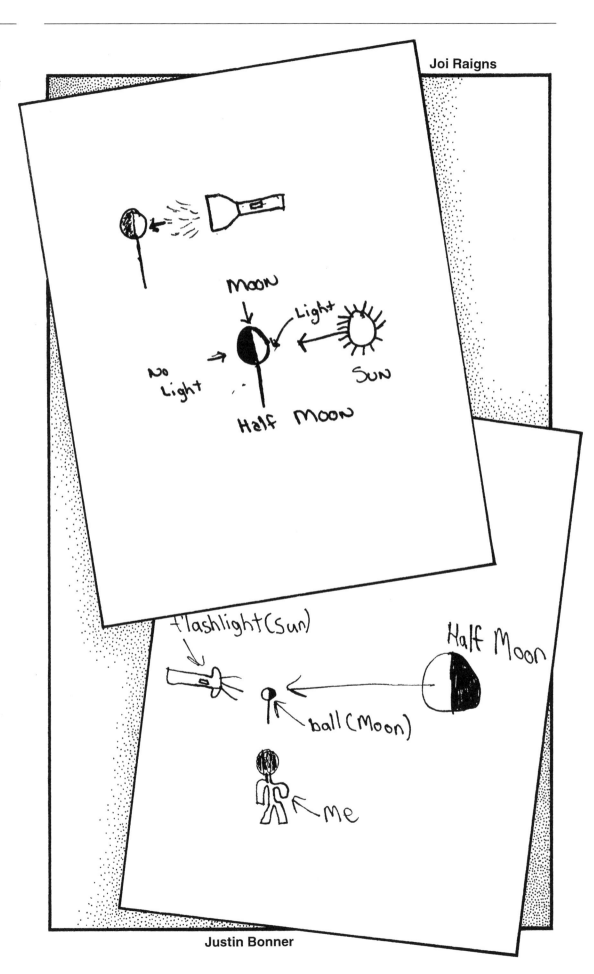

Section II: Investigating Invented Clocks

<table>
<tr><td>

LESSON 7

</td><td>

Using Water to Measure Time

</td></tr>
</table>

Overview and Objectives

In this first lesson of **Section II: Investigating Time with Invented Clocks,** students investigate one way to use water to measure time. They construct a sinking water clock capable of timing an interval of 15 seconds, and they begin identifying the variables involved in determining how rapidly or slowly the clock sinks. In Lessons 8 and 9, students will plan and conduct an investigation of how changing one of the variables affects the time it takes a funnel to sink. This cycle of exploration and investigation will be repeated in Lessons 10, 11, and 12, when students plan and conduct experiments with pendulums.

- Students construct sinking water clocks.

- Students identify the variables that have an effect on the time it takes their water clocks to sink.

- Students read about water clocks used by early cultures.

Background

This lesson marks the beginning of a new section of the unit. In this section, instead of observing the natural cycles of the sun and the moon, students begin to manipulate variables to change the rate at which observable events, such as sinking objects and swinging pendulums, take place. This shift in focus corresponds with the historical shift in timekeeping methods that occurred when people first looked for improvements to the methods that relied on the sun and moon. Through ongoing observations of the moon's phases and appropriate reading selections, students will be given a context for comparing timekeeping methods.

For your information, background about the history of water clocks has been included below. The **Reading Selection** on pg. 71 of the Teacher's Guide and pg. 30 of the Student Activity Book includes additional information.

Water clocks have been in use in one form or another for more than three thousand years. They were developed to meet a real need: how to tell time on cloudy days and at night. First used in Egypt and Babylonia, water clocks were brought across the Mediterranean by the Greeks. The Greeks called water clocks **klepsydra,** which means "thief of water."

The use of water clocks shifted people's thinking about time. Sun clocks were good for telling the time of day, but water clocks could be used easily to measure the length of shorter intervals of time. For example, in ancient Greece, citizens were allotted a certain amount of time—measured by sinking water clocks—to address the Senate or a jury. In China and in the Middle East, people created very elaborate water clocks. The most elaborate used gears and simple machines.

Materials

For each student

1 science notebook
1 piece of aluminum foil, 10 cm (4″) square

For every two students

1 plastic flex tank, 4 liters (1 gal), with water
3 brass washers, 9 mm (⅜″) diameter

For the class

1 clock with a sweep second hand
1 class list, "What We Know about Measuring Time" (from Lesson 1), and a marker of a different color from previous entries
3 buckets with handles, each approx. 4 liters (1 gal)
Several sponges
Several sheets of newsprint and marker(s)

Preparation

1. Cut one 10-cm (4″) square piece of aluminum foil for each student.

2. Fill each plastic tank about three-fourths full with water. You may want to ask students to help with this task. If your classroom is not equipped with a sink, buckets with handles are one way to transport and pour water efficiently.

3. Display a clock with a sweep second hand in the classroom.

Procedure

1. Remind students to continue recording their observations of the moon for the next several weeks. The record of moon observations will be important evidence of the pattern of the moon's phases.

2. Ask students to describe some of the problems they encountered using the sun and moon to keep track of time. Here are some of the things they are likely to come up with:

   - It is impossible to tell time when it is dark or cloudy.

   - Sun clocks aren't portable.

   - It is hard to be precise.

3. Show students the "What We Know about Measuring Time" list from Lesson 1. Ask students whether the list includes ways to keep track of time without depending only on the sun or moon. Encourage them to brainstorm new ideas to add to the list.

4. Explain to students that because people had problems keeping time with the sun and moon, they began to make different types of clocks. One type—sinking water clocks—used objects sinking in water to keep track of the passage of time.

5. Ask students to discuss with their partners their ideas about how to use water to keep track of time. Have them sketch a few possible designs in their notebooks and write explanations for their sketches.

6. Now ask students to use a piece of aluminum foil and brass washers to construct a sinking water clock. Challenge them to try to find a way to make a clock that will sink in 15 seconds. Have students use the clock on the wall to compare how long it takes their water clocks to sink. Encourage a variety of designs.

Figure 7-1

Constructing a
sinking water clock

7. Distribute the materials to students. Ask them to take turns testing their
    sinking clocks. Encourage them to talk with each other about what they are
    trying to accomplish.

8. After students have completed their work with water clocks, ask them to
    return the materials to the storage area and dry off their work area.

9. Have students describe and illustrate in their notebooks how they made
    their sinking water clocks. What worked? What didn't work?

Final Activities

1. Discuss with students the various strategies they used to construct their
    water clocks. Have students share one of their designs. Ask questions such
    as the following to focus the discussion. List students' responses on a sheet
    of newsprint.

    ■   What are some things you did to make the clock sink more quickly?
        More slowly?

■ How do you know that your sinking clock is consistent—that it sinks at the same rate each time?

■ How would you change your clock if you did this activity again?

Note: Save this class list to use in Lesson 8.

2. Explain that the things students changed to make the clock sink faster or slower are called **variables**, because they are able to be "varied." Tell students that in the next two lessons they will plan and conduct an experiment with sinking water clocks. The experiment will provide evidence of what happens when one variable is changed. Students can use this evidence to design different kinds of sinking water clocks.

3. Ask students to read "Water Clocks," on pg. 30 of the Student Activity Book (pg. 71 of the Teacher's Guide). Ask them to focus on the following questions as they read.

■ What are some advantages and disadvantages of water clocks compared with sun clocks?

■ What are some types of water clocks that have been invented other than those that sink?

Extensions

1. Encourage students to design and build timers that use water to keep track of the passage of time. Ask them to explain and demonstrate their timers for the rest of the class.

2. Ask students to create advertisements to sell their sinking water clocks. Have them include at least three good reasons why someone should buy them.

Assessment

This lesson is the first of a sequence of three lessons involving the investigation of sinking water clocks and the planning and carrying out of water clock experiments.

The specific process skills involved in these three lessons are listed below.

■ Planning an experiment

■ Identifying and controlling variables

■ Collecting and interpreting data

■ Presenting results in graph form

Because development of these skills requires practice, students apply them again with pendulums in Lessons 10, 11, and 12.

At the end of Lesson 9, you will have information with which to assess students' ability to plan and conduct an experiment. For example, the plan and graph students construct in Lessons 8 and 9 will provide information about questions such as the following.

■ Is the plan reasonable? Can the students do it?

■ Do students select one and only one variable to investigate? Have students controlled all but one variable in carrying out their experiments?

■ Do the experiments carry out the plan?

■ Are the graphs that students construct labeled?

By comparing your assessment of students' skills at the end of Lesson 9 with your assessment at the end of Lesson 12, you may be able to document changes in students' skill development.

Reading Selection

Water Clocks

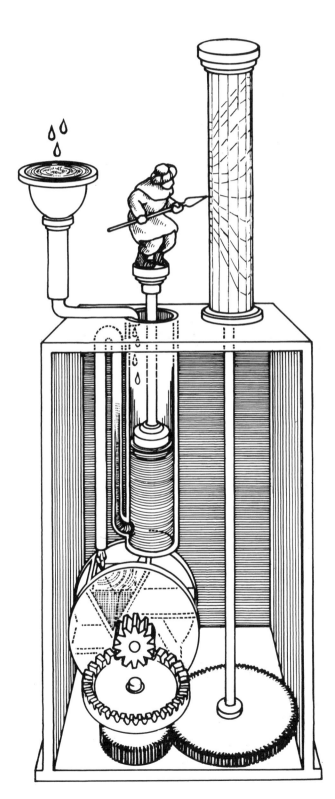

Egyptian water clock

People have used many different kinds of water clocks throughout the ages. Some were technical wonders; others were as simple as bowls with holes in them.

One of the earliest sinking clocks was devised by the Saxons, a Germanic people who conquered England in the fifth century. The Saxon clock was a bronze bowl with a hole in the bottom, designed to sink at a steady pace in a pool of water. The length of time it took for the bowl to sink became the Saxon's standard unit of time.

At the time of the Roman Empire, the Egyptians were making elaborate flowing water clocks, such as the one on the left. This particular clock, which was constructed in Alexandria, Egypt, could measure 24-hour days and 365-day years. As the water flowed into a chamber and the pointer rose, it showed on the cylinder what hour it was, and, at the end of the day, how far they had come in the passage of a year.

Later, toward the end of the early Middle Ages, the Chinese were telling time with a water-wheel clock. The most well-known Chinese water-wheel clock was designed by a man named Su Song, and it was 40 feet high. The Chinese believed that time, like flowing water, has no beginning and no end. The wheel shape of Su Song's clock reflected that belief. This clock could mark the passage of hours and quarter hours.

Other cultures used dripping water clocks. For example, the Romans were known to use clay pots, one suspended above the other, to keep track of how much time had passed. And they figured out one way to keep the water flowing from the upper container into the lower container at a fairly consistent and reliable rate. When the flow quickened because the opening in the clay pot had eroded, they lined the opening with gold or jewels so that the opening would stay the same size. (This design innovation has continued; today, jewels are used for the parts of watches that get a lot of wear.)

But there were other drawbacks to water clocks. There were times of drought, which meant that no water was available. And, too often, the clocks were unreliable because the temperature of the water had changed, making the water flow faster or more slowly. By the end of the Middle Ages in Europe, it was just these kinds of drawbacks that encouraged people to invent clocks that didn't depend on water.

Chinese water-wheel clock

Planning an Experiment with Sinking Water Clocks

Overview and Objectives

Working with sinking water clocks, students learn how to plan an experiment. They explore what happens to the water clock's "sinking time" when one variable is changed. The planning activities in this lesson prepare students to conduct their experiments in Lesson 9.

■ Students identify experimental variables affecting sinking water clocks.

■ Students plan an experiment controlling variables.

■ Students devise a data table to record their test data.

Background

In contrast with Lesson 7's activity, today's activity—planning an experiment—may seem unnecessary to some students. Many students are of course eager to get their hands wet and investigate the materials. But planning experiments is necessary. It is important that students see that careful planning gives shape to their experiments and that it is part of the process of discovery.

In Lesson 7 (**Final Activities,** Step 1), students identified several ways to change some variables that affect the rate at which objects sink. The list probably included some of the following ideas:

■ Number of holes

■ Weight

■ Size of the hole

■ Size of the container

■ Shape of the container

Each of these variables has a significant and observable effect on the rate at which the water clock sinks. The materials described in this lesson and Lesson 9 are designed to focus students' attention on three of these variables: weight (number of washers), size of the hole (different-sized beads), and the size of the container (different-sized funnels). These three were chosen because they are relatively straightforward to investigate and because students find them interesting. Other variables, such as the depth of the water or its temperature, are more difficult to measure, but they, too, may be identified by students. If students are interested in exploring these variables, encourage them to investigate them as well.

Components of Productive Experiments

Any experiment is successful if the researcher learns something in the process. Sometimes the researcher learns that a particular variable has no effect on the phenomenon being investigated, and this is a useful result. On the other hand, the researcher may learn that the variables he or she thought were unimportant are significant. The following list highlights some of the components of experiments that are likely to produce useful information. Students will practice and learn many of these components as they plan and conduct experiments in Lessons 8 through 12.

■ The researcher develops a good plan and follows it.

■ The researcher gathers information on the topic either through reading or talking with experts.

■ The researcher manipulates only one variable at a time.

■ The researcher makes careful observations over a period of time.

■ The researcher increases confidence in the results by doing each experimental trial a number of times and averaging the results.

■ The researcher refines the experiment by making changes in the apparatus, the procedures, or the way data is collected. Then, the researcher repeats the whole experiment.

■ The researcher keeps records—accurately, honestly, and regularly.

■ The researcher communicates the findings of the experiment to others.

Materials

For each student

   1   science notebook
   1   copy of **Record Sheet 8-B: Outlining the Team's Experiment**

For every two students

   1   copy of **Record Sheet 8-A: Experiment Planning Sheet**
   1   plastic tank, 4 liters (1 gal)
   1   large funnel
   1   bead-tube (yellow), 4-mm hole
   3   brass washers, 9 mm (⅜") diameter

For the class

   1   clock with a sweep second hand
   1   class list of variables (from Lesson 7)
   3   buckets with handles, 4 liters (1 gal)
   5   sets of two funnels (1 small and 1 medium)
   5   sets of bead-tubes (2-mm hole, 3-mm hole, and no hole)
  15   brass washers, 9 mm (⅜") diameter
       Several sponges
       Several sheets of newsprint and a marker

Preparation

1. Duplicate one copy of **Record Sheet 8-A: Experiment Planning Sheet** for every two students and one copy of **Record Sheet 8-B: Outlining the Team's Experiment** for each student.

2. Fill each tank about three-fourths full with water. You may want to ask students to help with this task.

3. Display in the classroom the list of variables from Lesson 7 (**Final Activities, Step 1**) and a clock with a sweep second hand.

Procedure

1. Remind students to continue observing the moon and recording the observations of the moon's phases.

2. Review with students the class list of variables about water clocks from the last lesson. Ask them to pick three of these variables and predict in their notebooks how changing each of the variables separately will affect the sinking time.

   For example, ask students what effect they predict poking additional holes in the container will have on the time it takes to sink. Have students include the reasons for their predictions.

3. Explain to students that they will be working with new materials today: a funnel, a bead-tube, and washers. They will be working with a partner to measure the time it takes for a water clock constructed from these materials to sink. Then they will plan an experiment to test one of their predictions about sinking water clocks.

4. Show students a funnel and a bead-tube. Challenge them to measure how long it takes this clock to sink with three washers attached, as shown in Figure 8-1.

Figure 8-1

Materials used to construct sinking water clocks

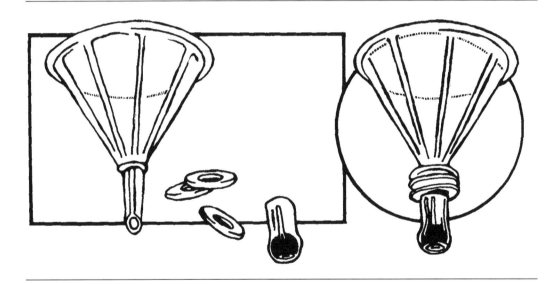

5. Distribute a funnel, a yellow bead-tube (4-mm hole), and three washers to each pair of students. Allow them some time to become familiar with these materials before asking them to focus on measuring the time it takes the funnel to sink. Ask each group to conduct several trials to obtain a sinking time. If the sinking times from the trials are inconsistent, the group will have to determine the one time that best represents its results. Let the students know that each group will be putting its sinking time on a class graph.

6. Now ask students to put the materials away so they will not be distracted while discussing their findings.

Figure 8-2

Measuring the time it takes the funnel to sink

7. Ask students to share their measurements of the sinking time. Invite students to suggest ways to record the class results so that the information is well organized. Use students' suggestions to construct a sample data table. Point out that data tables are useful for recording and organizing information when conducting experiments.

8. Have each group plot its data on a class frequency graph. This will help illustrate the need for repeated trials, because all of the times will not be exactly the same. It also will give students practice graphing data. Figure 8-3 shows a sample data table and frequency graph.

9. Now that students have had practice measuring the time it takes the "clock" to sink, ask them to work with a partner to plan an experiment. Ask them to use **Record Sheet 8-A: Experiment Planning Sheet,** to help them decide which variable they will investigate. Then show students the materials they can use to manipulate the variables: different-sized funnels (for varying container size), additional washers (for varying weight), and different-sized bead-tubes (for varying hole size).

10. Distribute a copy of **Record Sheet 8-B: Outlining the Team's Experiment,** to students who have picked a variable to test. The questions on the outline will help students focus on what they will be investigating in Lesson 9. Students who have never planned an experiment before may need help formulating the experimental question. You may want to assist them by providing a model or by suggesting several different beginnings. For example, ask them to fill in the blank in questions such as the following:

■ What will happen to the sinking time if the _____ is varied?

■ How does changing the _____ affect the _____?

Figure 8-3

Sample data table and line plot

Sample Data Table: The Time It Takes a Funnel to Sink

Conditions: Weight: 3 washers Hole Size: 4 mm (yellow bead) Funnel size: large	
Group	Sinking Time (in seconds)
1	23
2	20
3	22
4	20
5	22
6	19
7	22
8	21
9	22
10	22
11	25
12	23
13	21
14	22
15	21

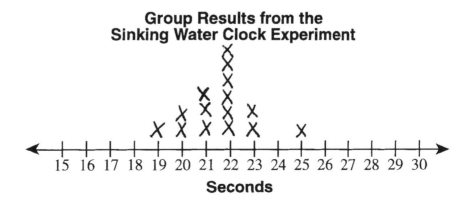

Group Results from the Sinking Water Clock Experiment

Seconds

Figure 8-4

*Students working
on planning sheets*

Final Activities

1. Ask students to construct a data table in their notebooks that they will use in Lesson 9 to record the sinking times of the funnel. Figure 8-5 shows several sample data tables.

   Note: If students have had a number of prior experiences conducting experiments, you may want to ask them to construct data tables without showing them a sample. If, however, this is new to students, a sample data table may prove to be a useful model for them to follow when conducting future experiments.

2. Ask each group to share briefly with the class how they are planning to conduct their experiment and what they predict they will find.

   Note: You will need to review the groups' plans in order to prepare the materials for Lesson 9. You may want to collect the record sheets and redistribute them at the beginning of Lesson 9.

Extensions

1. As a language arts activity, ask students to write analogies using the following sentence starter:

   A sinking clock is to time as a _____ is to _____.

2. The line plot encourages "mode," or the most frequent results, as the average. Ask students also to determine the average in terms of median (midpoint) and mean (the arithmetic average). Discuss which one students think is the best for reporting the results of this experiment.

Figure 8-5

*Sample
data tables*

Size of the Funnel	Sink Time (in seconds)			
	Trial 1	Trial 2	Trial 3	Average
Small				
Medium				
Large				

Hole Size	Sink Time (in seconds)			
	Trial 1	Trial 2	Trial 3	Average
7 mm (no beads)				
4 mm (yellow)				
3 mm (orange)				
2 mm (green)				

Weight (number of washers)	Sink Time (in seconds)			
	Trial 1	Trial 2	Trial 3	Average
1				
2				
3				
4				
5				
6				

Assessment

When reviewing the students' planning sheets, check to see whether they have done the following.

- Identified a specific, testable question involving the chosen variable
- Chosen one variable to test and listed the other variables as constants
- Identified something to measure
- Chosen a project that can be completed
- Devised a workable plan
- Created a table for recording their data

This information will be particularly useful for comparison with students' planning abilities in Lesson 10.

Record Sheet 8-A

Names: _____

Date: _____

Experiment Planning Sheet

Question we are trying to answer:

Variable we will vary (change):

Variables we will hold constant:

Procedure:

Record Sheet 8-B

Name: _____

Date: _____

Outlining the Team's Experiment

1. The question we will try to answer: _____

_____

_____

2. The one variable we will test: _____

3. In order to make our experiment a fair test, we will keep all of these variables constant (unchanged):

   ■ _____

   ■ _____

   ■ _____

   ■ _____

   ■ _____

4. Will we need special materials or equipment? _____

   If so, we will need _____

   _____

5. What we will measure: _____

   _____

   _____

6. What we will count: _____

   _____

   _____

7. What we will observe: _____

   _____

   _____

8. What we think will happen (our hypothesis): _____

   _____

   _____

Experimenting with Sinking Water Clocks

Overview and Objectives

Today students conduct the sinking water clock experiments they planned in Lesson 8. By manipulating one variable and measuring the time it takes the clocks to sink, students learn that they can adjust the rate at which sinking occurs. They collect and graph the data from their experiments and discuss their findings. These activities help prepare students for experiments with pendulums in Lessons 10, 11, and 12.

- Students conduct the experiments they planned in Lesson 8.

- Students construct a graph to summarize their findings.

- Students interpret and discuss their experimental results.

Background

The process of conducting an experiment is exciting. Researchers often learn many new and unexpected things. Examples of several unplanned student discoveries about water clocks are listed below.

- The funnels sink very fast if they are turned upside down. (You can feel the air coming out.)

- If the water isn't deep enough, the funnels won't sink because they hit bottom.

- With no washers attached, the funnels won't sink all the way.

- It takes much longer for the funnels to fill up and sink than it does for them to empty out.

The activities in this lesson are based on the plans that students developed in Lesson 8. They will find that large funnels take longer to sink than small funnels; additional washers shorten the time it takes a funnel to sink; and the larger the opening, the shorter the sinking time.

Students probably will find this experiment fascinating, and they may want to alter their plans so that they can explore further. It is important, however, to help students recognize the need to carry out the plan they have developed, while also encouraging them to explore new questions.

Constructing Graphs

Throughout this unit, students are asked to construct graphs of their recorded data. Graphing is a practical application of a math skill that they have studied. The graph grid provided in this lesson was designed for students who have some experience constructing graphs but who are not yet expert at labeling axes, defining the scale, or writing titles. In Lessons 11 and 12, students will be asked to provide some of this information themselves.

Students who have had more experience constructing graphs should be encouraged to determine what type of graph best represents their data. If available, computer spread sheets and graphing packages could be used.

Materials

For each student

  1 science notebook

  1 completed copy of **Record Sheet 8-B: Outlining the Team's Experiment** (from Lesson 8)

  1 copy of **Record Sheet 9-A: Graphing Sinking Water Clocks**

For every two students

  1 completed copy of **Record Sheet 8-A: Experiment Planning Sheet** (from Lesson 8)

  1 plastic tank, 4 liters (1 gal)

  1 large funnel

  1 bead-tube (yellow), 4-mm hole

  3 brass washers, 9 mm (⅜″) diameter

For the class

  1 clock with a sweep second hand

  3 buckets with handles, 4 liters (1 gal)

     Several sponges

For groups varying the hole size

  1 bead-tube (green), 2-mm hole

  1 bead-tube (orange), 3-mm hole

  1 bead-tube, no bead

For groups varying the weight of the container

  3 additional brass washers, 9 mm (⅜″) diameter

For groups varying the size of the container

  1 small funnel

  1 medium funnel

Preparation

1. Examine each group's experimental plan outline from Lesson 8. Arrange the materials so that each group has materials that match its plan.

2. Duplicate one copy of **Record Sheet 9-A: Graphing Sinking Water Clocks** for each student.

Procedure

1. Review with students the information they will be collecting as they conduct their experiments. First, ask them to read over the experimental outlines and planning sheets that they completed in Lesson 8. You may want to have students exchange and discuss their plans with another pair of students because review by a "third party" often is helpful in determining whether or not the plan makes sense.

2. Ask students to find in their notebooks the data table they prepared in Lesson 8 and remind them to record the sinking times on it. Suggest that they pick one data table to use for recording their results.

3. Ask students to get the materials they will need and to begin their investigations. Have students construct the same basic clock as in Lesson 8 (large funnel, yellow bead-tube, 3 washers) and then begin altering the variable they have selected. Remind students to repeat each of the trials several times to see whether or not their results are consistent.

Figure 9-1

Students conducting the experiment and recording their results

4. After students have finished investigating, ask each student to use the information he or she has collected to construct a graph on **Record Sheet 9-A**.

5. When students have completed their graphs, display them on a wall or bulletin board. Arrange the displayed graphs so that they are grouped by variable.

6. Arrange the groups so that they may discuss the experiment with another group that investigated the same variable. Ask group members to explain what they did and what they observed to the other groups.

7. Next, have the groups discuss their experiment with a group that investigated a different variable. Again, ask them to explain what they did and what they observed.

Final Activities

1. Ask each student to write and illustrate a letter to someone in his or her family describing the group's experiment. Have students include the following in their letters:

   ■ The question they investigated

   ■ The procedure they used

   ■ The evidence they found

   ■ Information about how to build a sinking water clock

   Explain that it is especially important for students to explain carefully what they did because the reader was not there to observe the experiment.

2. As a class, discuss ways of making water clocks capable of timing very long or very short intervals of time. Encourage students to use information they learned by doing these experiments. This discussion will tell you whether students understand the correlation between changing the variables and lengthening or shortening the sinking time.

Extensions

1. Encourage students to design and construct a sinking water clock using other materials. Challenge them to adjust or place marks on their clock so that it measures a certain amount of time consistently. For example, ask students to build a clock to measure the duration of the lunch period, recess, or the time it takes to accomplish certain household chores.

2. Use a computer graphing program to make a class pie graph showing the percentage of students who tested each of the variables.

3. Find the average and range for identical tests conducted by different groups of students. For example, ask students who measured the sinking time for a large funnel with three washers and a 2-mm bead-tube attached to share their data and to find the best way to report the average of all of their measurements.

Assessment

The conclusion of this lesson is a natural point at which to assess students' performance over the last three lessons. Work products include the following:

   ■ Outlines of each team's experiment

   ■ Data tables, graphs, and the letters written describing the experiments

This work will help you assess the strengths and weaknesses of students in planning, conducting, and communicating the results of an experiment. In particular, look for evidence that students have

- Followed the plan they developed in Lesson 8

- Conducted repeated trials

- Recorded data accurately, honestly, and consistently

- Constructed graphs using the data they recorded on their data tables

- Interpreted the data that they have collected

Comparing students' performance in this sequence of lessons with that in Lessons 10, 11, and 12 will provide you with information with which to assess their progress in planning, conducting, and communicating the results of an experiment.

Record Sheet 9-A

Name: _____

Date: _____

Graphing Sinking Water Clocks

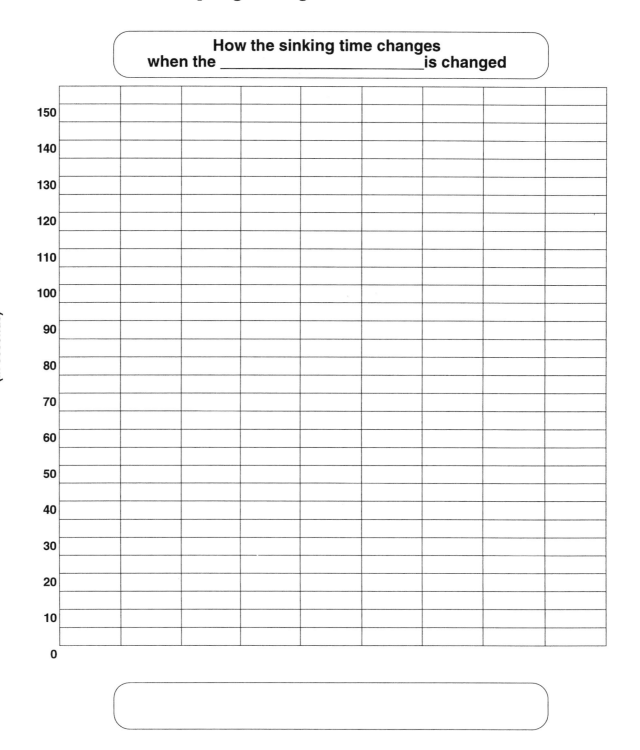

How the sinking time changes
when the _____is changed

Sinking Time (in seconds)

150
140
130
120
110
100
90
80
70
60
50
40
30
20
10
0

Investigating Pendulums

Overview and Objectives

Pendulums were an innovation in the historical development of timekeeping devices. They are not dependent on the weather, as sun clocks are, and they are less cumbersome than water clocks. In this lesson, students begin to investigate the characteristics of pendulums. As they did in their investigations of sinking water clocks, students identify variables and plan an experiment. In Lesson 11, students will conduct the experiment they have planned, and in Lesson 12, they will repeat the experiments of other students and compare results.

- Students identify characteristics of pendulums.

- Students plan an experiment to investigate how changing one variable affects the frequency of a pendulum.

Background

The history of timekeeping is really the search for less cumbersome and more precise timing devices. Sundials, water clocks, and then sand timers were each refined and improved many times, but each had serious problems.

In 1583, Galileo Galilei made an important discovery that led to a new way of keeping time. Watching a pendulum chandelier swing back and forth in the breeze at the Cathedral of Pisa, Galileo realized that the pendulum could serve as a regular timing device. This led to the development of mechanical clocks regulated by swinging pendulums and escapement mechanisms. Students will construct and investigate one such mechanism in Lessons 13, 14, and 15.

Three things are required to make a simple pendulum: a piece of string, a heavy object tied to the end of the string, and a place to hang the string so that the object can swing back and forth freely. Figure 10-1 shows a simple pendulum. The object at the end of a pendulum is called a **bob**, perhaps because of its bobbing motion.

The **frequency** of a pendulum is the number of back-and-forth swings it makes in a certain length of time. By counting the number of back-and-forth swings that occur in 30 seconds, students can measure the frequency directly. By convention, one swing—over and back—is usually counted as a complete cycle.

The reason pendulums are useful in timekeeping is that the frequency can be changed by varying the length of the pendulum. Longer pendulums swing with a lower frequency than shorter pendulums. Interestingly, changing the mass of the pendulum bob does not affect the frequency of the pendulum. And changing the starting angle of the pendulum (how far you pull it back to get it started) has only a very slight effect on the frequency.

Figure 10-1

Simple pendulum

Many students believe wholeheartedly that changing any of the above variables will change the frequency of a pendulum. So conducting experiments to investigate the effect of any one of them is a valuable experience. This experience will help students learn that discovering which variables have **no** effect on frequency is as important as exploring the observable effect caused by changing the pendulum's length.

Note: In Lesson 12, students will have an opportunity to repeat the experiments that other students conduct in Lesson 11. This will give them some insight into the cooperative nature of scientific inquiry. Experiments are repeated and results compared—a cooperative venture with the goal of learning new things. Often the result is more questions, which need to be answered through more investigations.

Materials

For each student

- 1 science notebook
- 1 copy of **Record Sheet 10-B: Outlining the Team's Experiment**

For every two students

- 1 cardboard pendulum support, 10 cm (4″) square
- 1 tape measure
- 1 paper protractor (from blackline master on pg. 106)
- 1 large washer, 4 cm (1½″) diameter
- 1 jumbo paper clip
- 1 string, 1.5 m (5 ft) long
- 1 copy of **Record Sheet 10-A: Experiment Planning Sheet**

For the class

    1   clock with a sweep second hand

    1   pair of scissors

        Newsprint and marker

Preparation

1. Cut one piece of string 1.5 m (60″) long for each pair of students.

2. Display the wall clock in the classroom.

3. Duplicate one copy of **Record Sheet 10-A: Experiment Planning Sheet** for every two students and one copy of **Record Sheet 10-B: Outlining the Team's Experiment** for each student.

4. Duplicate the **Blackline Master: Paper Protractors** on pg. 106 and cut out enough protractors so that each student pair will have one.

Procedure

1. Remind students to continue posting their observations of the moon's phases.

2. Ask students to make a class list of some of the disadvantages of using water clocks to measure the passage of time. The list will probably include some of the following:

   ■ The water will freeze if it gets cold enough.

   ■ Evaporation might cause the clock to run dry. More water needs to be added.

   ■ Water is heavy, so water clocks are difficult to move around.

3. Ask students to discuss ways to overcome some of the problems with water clocks. Then ask students to describe some of the pendulum clocks they have seen.

4. Ask students how the consistent back-and-forth swinging of pendulums could be used to keep track of the passage of time. Many students will respond that one way is counting the pendulum's swings.

5. Challenge students to work with a partner to find out how many back-and-forth swings a pendulum makes in 30 seconds. Then distribute the materials. Before beginning the activity, students must assemble their pendulums. Instructions for assembling a pendulum are included on pg. 103 (pg. 41 of the Student Activity Book).

6. After completing the activity, have students return their pendulums to the storage area (they will use them in the next two lessons) and report on the number of swings they counted in 30 seconds. Explain that this number is a measure of how frequently the pendulum swings back and forth. This measurement is called the **frequency**. On the chalkboard or on a sheet of newsprint, record the frequency that each group reports. The frequencies probably will range from about 15 cycles per 30 seconds to almost 40 per 30 seconds.

7. Now that students have had some experience with pendulums, ask them to begin considering the variables involved. Ask students to discuss with their partners and another group of students their ideas about what caused the pendulums to swing at such different frequencies. Remind them that they have had experience identifying variables. In Lesson 7, for example, they identified the variables they thought would affect how fast a water clock would sink.

8. Ask students to report on their discussions to the class. On a sheet of newsprint, make a class list of pendulum variables to investigate. The list will probably include some of the following:

- Weight of the pendulum bob
- Length of the pendulum
- Shape or size of the pendulum bob
- Type of string used to support the bob
- Starting angle used to start the pendulum swinging
- Amount of "push" used to start the pendulum swinging

9. Distribute a copy of **Record Sheet 10-A: Experiment Planning Sheet,** to each pair of students. Ask them to use it to decide which variable they will investigate. Explain to students that they will have an opportunity to repeat the experiments conducted by other groups after they complete their own investigation.

10. As students decide on a variable to test, distribute a copy of **Record Sheet 10-B: Outlining the Team's Experiment**. Encourage students to be as specific as possible in developing the plan for their experiment. For example, ask them to consider how they will measure the pendulum's starting angle, its weight, or its length (see Figure 10-2). This is a good time to distribute the paper protractors and the tape measures. Suggest that one person in each pair keep the protractor in his or her notebook to use over the next three lessons.

Note: Some students may still need a model to assist them in formulating the experimental question. A question such as the following will help them get started: What will happen to the frequency of the pendulum if the _____ is varied?

Final Activities

1. Ask students to construct a data table in their notebooks that they will use in Lesson 11 to record the frequency of the pendulum after changing the experimental variable. Figure 10-3 shows three sample data tables. If students are having difficulty constructing a data table, remind them to review the data tables they used to organize their sinking water clock data in Lessons 8 and 9.

2. Ask each group to share briefly with the class how they are planning to conduct their experiment and what they predict they will find.

Note: You will need to review the groups' plans in order to prepare the materials for Lesson 9. You may want to collect the record sheets and redistribute them at the beginning of Lesson 11.

Figure 10-2

Experimenting with the pendulum's starting angle, its weight, and its length

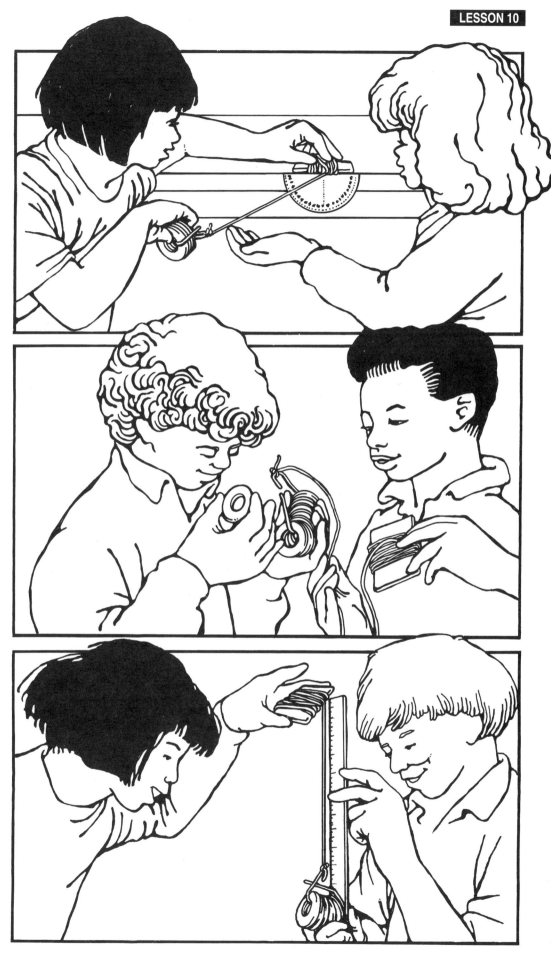

Figure 10-3

Three sample data tables

How the Length of the String Affects Frequency

Length of the String (cm)	Frequency (Number of Swings in 30 Seconds)			
	Trial 1	Trial 2	Trial 3	Average

How the Mass Affects Frequency

Pendulum Mass (number of washers)	Frequency (Number of Swings in 30 Seconds)			
	Trial 1	Trial 2	Trial 3	Average
1				
2				
3				
4				
5				
6				

Figure 10-3
(continued)

How the Pendulum's Starting Angle Affects Frequency

Starting Angle (degrees)	Frequency (Number of Swings in 30 Seconds)			
	Trial 1	Trial 2	Trial 3	Average
10				
20				
30				
40				
50				
60				

Extensions

1. Ask students to measure the frequency of a swing in the playground with another student on it. How many back-and-forth swings does the student make in 30 seconds? How many back-and-forth swings does the swing make with two students on it? How many with nobody on it? Ask them to compare their observations with the frequency of the pendulum they measured in the classroom. This activity may help students focus on the possible causes for differences in frequency.

2. Investigate how a metronome is used to keep time in music. (You should be able to obtain one from a music teacher.) Or, ask several student-musicians to discuss the role of time and counting in music.

3. Create a box-and-whisker plot for the frequencies obtained in Step 6 of the **Procedure** section. This type of graph is particularly effective in illustrating the median and range of data. Write down the frequencies in serial order (for example, 15, 21, 24, 29, 30, 30, 31, 32, 32, 33, 33, 34, 35, 37, 39). On the box-and-whisker plot shown in Figure 10-4, the data from the lower quartile (29) to the upper quartile (34) are represented with a box; the data below the lower quartile and above the upper quartile are represented with horizontal lines, or "whiskers." The median (32) is represented with a vertical line in the box.

Figure 10-4

Sample box-and-whisker plot

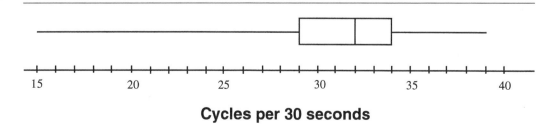

Cycles per 30 seconds

Assessment

Review the experiment planning sheets that students have completed. As in Lesson 8, check whether students have done the following:

- Chosen one variable to test and listed the other variables as constants
- Identified a specific, testable question involving the chosen variable
- Identified something to measure
- Chosen a project that can be completed
- Devised a workable plan
- Created a table for recording their data

This information will be particularly useful for comparison with students' work from Lesson 8. Look for evidence that students' skill in planning an experiment has increased. Specific evidence of this may include such things as the following:

- Statements that are worded more carefully
- Greater attention to the details of the experiment, as listed above
- Well-organized and clearly labeled data tables
- Questions that reflect measurable events

Student Instructions for Making a Simple Pendulum

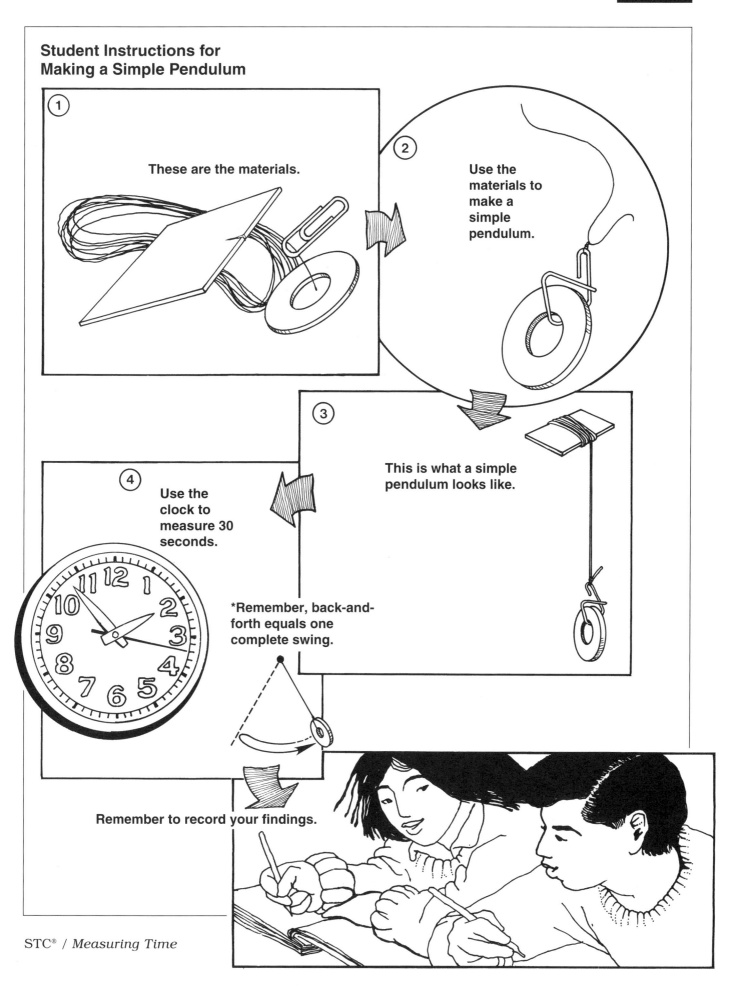

① These are the materials.

② Use the materials to make a simple pendulum.

③ This is what a simple pendulum looks like.

④ Use the clock to measure 30 seconds.

*Remember, back-and-forth equals one complete swing.

Remember to record your findings.

Record Sheet 10-A

Names: _____

Date: _____

Experiment Planning Sheet

Question we are trying to answer:

Variable we will vary (change):	**Variables we will hold constant:**

Procedure:

Record Sheet 10-B

Name: _____

Date: _____

Outlining the Team's Experiment

1. The question we will try to answer: _____

   _____

   _____

2. The one variable we will test: _____

3. In order to make our experiment a fair test, we will keep all of these
   variables constant (unchanged):

   ■ _____

   ■ _____

   ■ _____

   ■ _____

   ■ _____

4. Will we need special materials or equipment? _____
   If so, we will need _____

   _____

5. What we will measure: _____

   _____

   _____

6. What we will count: _____

   _____

   _____

7. What we will observe: _____

   _____

   _____

8. What we think will happen (our hypothesis): _____

   _____

   _____

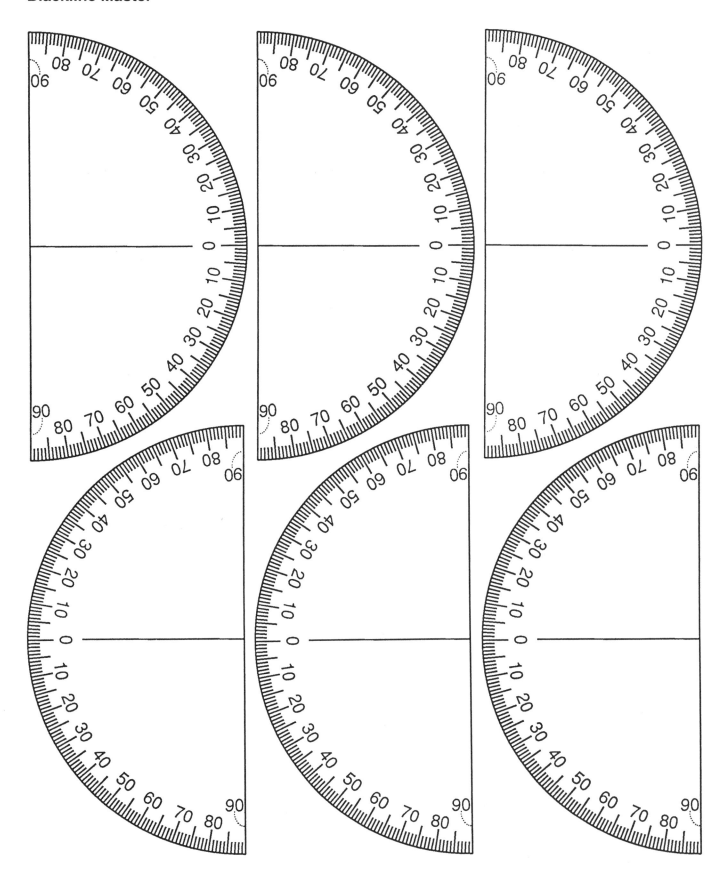

Experimenting with Pendulums

Overview and Objectives

By conducting the experiment they planned in Lesson 10, students can observe the effect of changing one variable on the frequency of a pendulum. The graphs they construct will enable them to post a summary of their findings for the rest of the class. Then teams can repeat the experiment and compare results in the next lesson.

- Students conduct the experiment they planned in Lesson 10.

- Students record their findings and construct individual graphs.

- Students explain their investigations to other students.

Background

As students conduct their experiments in this lesson, they will probably make many unplanned discoveries. As mentioned in Lesson 9, such discoveries are part of the excitement of scientific inquiry. Here are several examples:

- Pendulums swing almost as high as the height from which they are released.

- If pushed a certain way, pendulums can be made to swing in circles instead of back and forth.

- A pendulum with an extremely lightweight bob will slow down and stop much more quickly than one with a heavier bob.

- Shortening the string at the right moment can make the pendulum swing higher and higher (much as a person on a swing can control how high he or she swings).

In addition to unplanned discoveries such as these, students will observe that the mass of the bob and the position of the starting angle have no consistent effect on the pendulum's frequency. Some students may think that their experiment failed because they did not observe any change. They may even modify their observations to reflect what they expected. To help them see that experiments often produce unexpected results, students need to be encouraged to repeat their experiments in a consistent way. Then they will be able to identify patterns. They will also come to understand that experiments are not failures when something is learned from them.

Students who investigate the effect of changing the length of the pendulum will find that the length has a significant effect on the frequency. They will notice that longer pendulums swing with a lower frequency than shorter ones do.

The graph grid provided on pg. 113 (**Record Sheet 11-A**) requires greater student input than the graph produced in Lesson 9. By using this grid again in Lesson 12, students will continue to practice their graphing skills as they learn how to construct graphs on their own.

Materials

For each student

1   science notebook

1   completed copy of **Record Sheet 10-B: Outlining the Team's Experiment** (from Lesson 10)

1   copy of **Record Sheet 11-A: Graphing the Frequency of a Pendulum**

For every two students

1   copy of **Record Sheet 10-A: Experiment Planning Sheet** (from Lesson 10)

1   pendulum (from Lesson 10)

1   tape measure

1   paper protractor

For the class

1   clock with a sweep second hand

For groups varying the weight of the pendulum bob

6   additional large washers, 4 cm (1½″) diameter

For groups varying the length of the string

1   additional string, 2 m (6½ ft) long

Preparation

1. Examine each group's experimental outline from Lesson 10. Arrange the materials so that the groups will have materials that match their plans.

2. Duplicate one copy of **Record Sheet 11-A** for each student.

Procedure

1. Ask students to describe the information they will be collecting as they conduct the experiments they planned in Lesson 10. Have them review their experimental outlines and planning sheets.

2. Have students locate the data tables they prepared in Lesson 10. Remind them to record the frequency for the conditions that they investigate.

3. Ask students to record in their notebooks the variables of the experiment that they will keep constant. For example, the groups experimenting with changing the mass of the pendulum bob will keep both the length and starting angle constant.

4. Explain to students that they will have the opportunity to investigate other variables in the next lesson by repeating the experiments of other groups.

5. Ask students to get the materials they need and begin their investigations. Remind students to conduct each of the trials at least three times to determine whether their results are consistent. (A group will be graphing only one frequency for each trial.)

Figure 11-1

Conducting the experiment

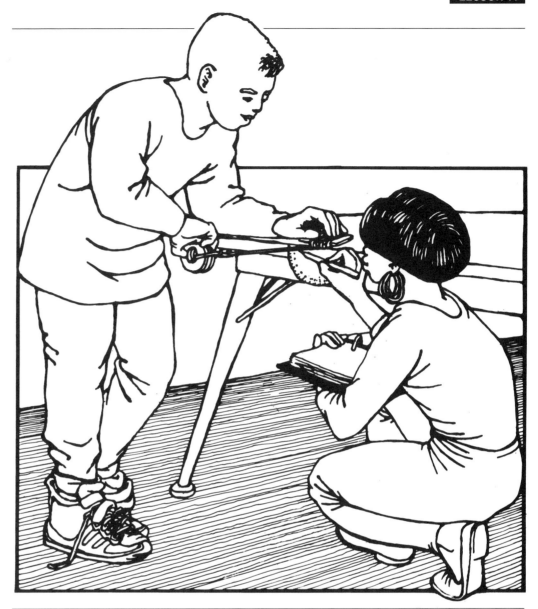

6. After students complete their experiments, have them return the materials to the storage area.

7. Ask each student to use the information he or she has collected to construct a graph on **Record Sheet 11-A**.

8. Display students' completed graphs on a wall or bulletin board. Display the graphs by variable.

Final Activities

1. Arrange students so that each group can discuss their experiment, including the plan they developed, with a group that investigated a different variable. Ask them to explain the following:

   - How they conducted the experiment

   - What they observed

   - What they discovered

   - What questions the experiment raises

2. As a class, discuss what each group learned about the frequency of pendulums. Remind students that in the next lesson they will use another group's experimental plan to conduct a different experiment.

Extension

Encourage students to describe the timekeeping characteristics of pendulums and water clocks. Then ask students to use a Venn diagram to compare pendulums with water clocks.

Record Sheet 11-A

Name: _____

Date: _____

Graphing the Frequency of a Pendulum

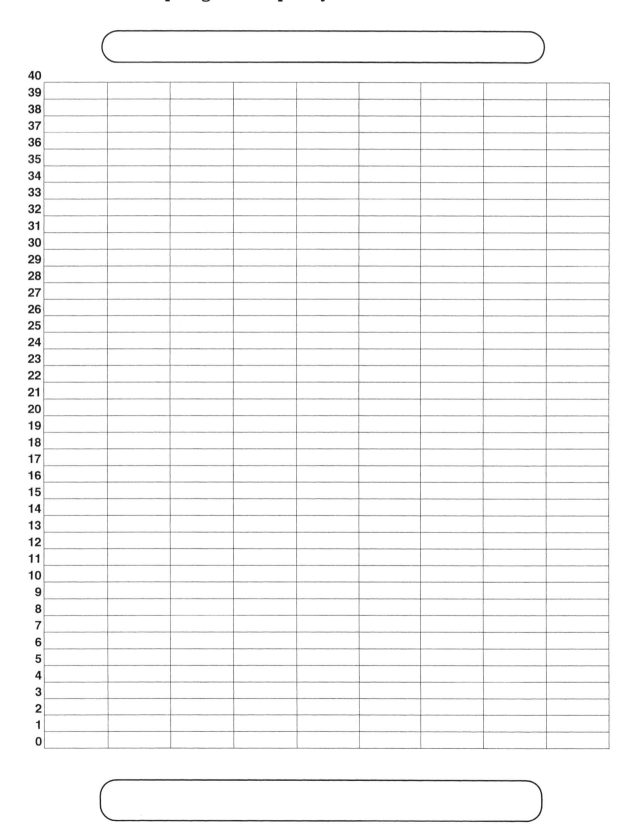

Number of Swings in 30 Seconds

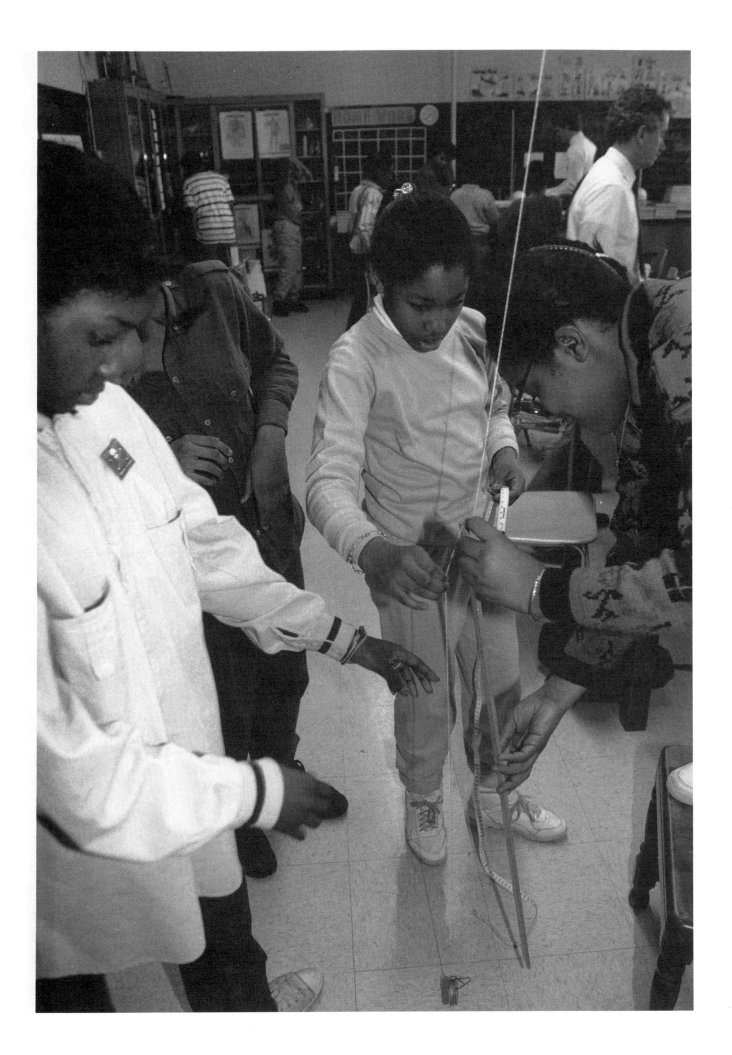

Comparing Results

Overview and Objectives

By repeating other groups' experiments, students can compare their results with those of other groups and discuss their findings and conclusions. This process also provides students with opportunities to observe that the frequency of a pendulum is consistently affected by changes in its length but not by changes in the mass of the bob or the starting angle of the swing.

- Students investigate the effect of a second variable on the frequency of a pendulum.

- Students discover that the frequency of a pendulum is not affected significantly by changes in mass or starting angle but is affected by changes in length.

Background

Students may have some difficulty making sense of what they are observing in an experimental situation. If their experience with certain phenomena is limited, they often make assumptions and draw conclusions that are contradicted by later observations. For example, students may have seen a heavy wrecking ball suspended from a long cable swinging slowly toward a building. They might have concluded that the great weight of the ball was the reason for the pendulum's slow swing rather than the length of the cable. So when they encounter a similar situation in the classroom, they may assume that weight and not length is responsible for the pendulum's frequency.

The point of the classroom activities is to provide students with opportunities to try out their ideas for themselves. By repeating their classmates' experiments, students are able to continue to question their previous assumptions or confirm their observations and expectations. Then they can discuss their ideas with other students. It is important to help students become familiar with a process through which they can discover answers for themselves. So encourage students to question repeatedly and to reexamine what they find. Then refocus students' attention on the critical factors and have them observe again.

Materials

For each student
1 science notebook
1 copy of **Record Sheet 12-A: Graphing the Frequency of a Pendulum**

For every two students

1. copy of another group's **Record Sheet 10-A: Experiment Planning Sheet** (from Lesson 10)
1. basic pendulum, from previous lessons (cardboard support, 1 large washer, 1 jumbo paper clip, and 1.5-m piece of string)
1. tape measure
1. paper protractor

For the class

1. clock with a sweep second hand
1. 3-washer pendulum, 3 m (10 ft) long

For groups varying the weight of the pendulum bob

6. additional large washers, 4 cm (1½") diameter

For groups varying the length of the string

1. additional string, 2 m (6½ ft) long

Preparation

1. Review the planning sheets that students prepared in Lesson 10. Then arrange the materials so that the groups can get materials that match the plans they are using.

2. Duplicate one copy of **Record Sheet 12-A: Graphing the Frequency of a Pendulum** for each student.

   Note: If some students finish their investigations quickly, encourage them to experiment with another variable and construct an additional graph.

Procedure

1. Review with students the process of investigation they used in Lesson 11. Tell them that they will repeat the process in this lesson. Ask students to exchange their **Record Sheet 10-B: Experiment Planning Sheet** for that of another group who altered a different variable.

2. Ask students to prepare data tables in their notebooks for the experiments they will conduct. Encourage them to ask students who have already conducted the experiment for advice.

3. Have students share with the class which variable they will be investigating and its predicted effect on the frequency of the pendulum. Ask them to record their predictions in their notebooks.

4. As they did in Lesson 11, remind students to record in their notebooks the conditions of the experiments that they will keep constant.

5. Ask students to get the materials they need and begin their investigations. Remind students to repeat each of the trials several times to determine whether their results are consistent.

6. After students complete their experiments, have them return the materials to the storage area.

7. Ask each student to use the information collected on the data table to construct a graph on **Record Sheet 12-A**. Again, remind students to plot the average frequency for each trial.

Figure 12-1

Students preparing
to repeat the
experiment of
another group

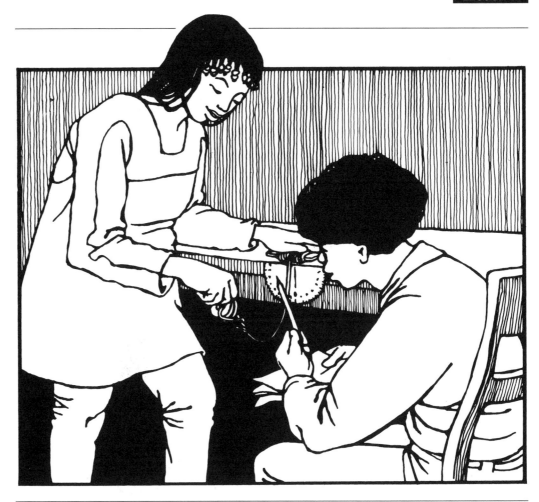

Final Activities

1. Hang a very long pendulum from the ceiling of the classroom, the top of the chalkboard, or another high support. Before adding the pendulum bob or swinging the pendulum, ask students to respond in their notebooks to the following questions:

   ■ Make a prediction. How do you think the frequency of this long pendulum will compare with the frequency of a shorter pendulum?

   ■ What are some reasons for your prediction?

2. Ask students to measure and record the frequency of the long pendulum by counting the number of back-and-forth swings it makes in 30 seconds. Have students measure the frequency three times.

3. Ask students to write and draw in their notebooks in response to the following questions:

   ■ How does the frequency of the very long pendulum compare with the frequency of shorter pendulums?

   ■ In what ways were you surprised by what you observed?

   Ask students to share what they have written with the rest of the class or with a small group of students.

Extensions

1. As an additional embedded assessment activity, ask students to predict how the frequency of the very long pendulum investigated in Step 1 of the **Final Activities** section will be affected by using a heavier pendulum bob, such as a large book. Have students record their predictions and the reasons for them and then measure and record the frequency of the heavier pendulum. Ask students to discuss their findings.

2. Ask students to read "Galileo and the Pendulum" on pg. 119 (pg. 50 in the Student Activity Book). Questions such as the following will help students focus on what they are reading:

    ■ What did Galileo discover about pendulums?

    ■ What are some ways that Galileo's investigation was similar to your investigations of pendulums?

3. Encourage students to find out more about a special type of pendulum—the Foucault pendulum. This device can be used to demonstrate that the earth rotates. Foucault pendulums are displayed in many museums throughout the United States.

4. Challenge students to specify the characteristics of a pendulum and to estimate the number of swings a particular pendulum would make in one hour, one day, and one year. Ask them to write in their notebooks how they calculated their estimates.

Assessment

This lesson is a natural point at which to compare students' experiments with water clocks and pendulums. Assess students' progress in some of the following areas:

■ Do students manipulate only one variable at a time when conducting experiments?

■ Are students' data tables organized?

■ Do students' graphs represent their data accurately?

■ Have students made progress in explaining their investigations to others?

Step 1 in the **Final Activities** section of this lesson is an embedded assessment designed to show the degree to which students understand that varying the length of a pendulum changes its frequency. Students' notebook entries and statements in class will allow you to assess the following points:

■ Are students able to formulate predictions about the frequency of a long pendulum and give specific reasons for their predictions?

■ Can students successfully communicate their observations and ideas?

■ Are students aware that a longer pendulum swings at a lower frequency than a shorter pendulum does?

Repeating a similar assessment activity after the conclusion of the unit may provide additional information about what individual students have learned. See **Appendix A** for more information and suggestions.

Reading Selection

Galileo and the Pendulum

When Galileo Galilei looked at the world around him, he often saw things no one else did. Because he made so many discoveries, many stories have been told about him over the years. Some of them are true, and some of them are only partially true.

This true story happened in 1583 in Pisa, Italy, a town famous for its university and cathedral. The cathedral had a bell tower, but part of it was sinking. (It became known as "The Leaning Tower of Pisa.") There are many stories about Galileo and the tower, but this story is about something that Galileo learned inside the cathedral.

One day, when Galileo was 19 years old, he noticed that the chandelier (it may have been an altar lamp) was swinging back and forth. Perhaps the wind was blowing it. What Galileo saw was that the chandelier swung back and forth not once but several times in a way that seemed, well, as regular as clockwork. Galileo decided to use his pulse to time how long it took the chandelier to swing back and forth.

By counting and watching carefully, Galileo made an important discovery. He found that the time it took the chandelier to make a complete swing was always the same. It didn't seem to matter if the chandelier was just barely moving or swinging back and forth vigorously. Galileo recognized that he could use any swinging object as a timekeeper.

He was the first person to understand that a pendulum was a simple and reliable way to keep time.

Some years later Galileo said that this discovery changed his life. When he noticed and timed the cathedral chandelier, he was a medical student at the University of Pisa. But he became so fascinated with pendulums and the way objects move that he gave up medicine to study mathematics and natural science.

Elaborating on what he had seen, Galileo later designed a pendulum clock. Other people went on to make similar clocks, such as the grandfather clock.

Record Sheet 12-A

Name: _____

Date: _____

Graphing the Frequency of a Pendulum

Number of Swings in 30 Seconds

40
39
38
37
36
35
34
33
32
31
30
29
28
27
26
25
24
23
22
21
20
19
18
17
16
15
14
13
12
11
10
9
8
7
6
5
4
3
2
1
0

Constructing a Clock Escapement

Overview and Objectives

In the last three lessons, students investigated the characteristics of pendulums. Over the next three lessons, students will explore how a pendulum can be used to keep track of the passage of long periods of time. This is accomplished by using a mechanical device—an **escapement**—to keep the pendulum swinging. In this lesson, students follow a plan to assemble a clock escapement. This activity familiarizes students with the operation of the device and prepares them for further investigation. In Lesson 14, students learn to troubleshoot the escapement, and in Lesson 15 they are challenged to modify it and use it to measure time.

■ Students build a working model of an escapement.

■ Students become familiar with how an escapement works.

Background

Modern clocks constructed from pendulums, springs, or vibrating quartz crystals operated by microelectronic circuits have largely eliminated people's daily reliance on the sun and moon to keep track of time. But this transition did not occur overnight. Beginning with pendulum clocks driven by falling weights, scientists and engineers made gradual improvements to timekeeping devices in order to make them more accurate. The escapement mechanism that students work with in the next three lessons is an example of one such improvement.

An escapement is a device that delivers the energy to drive a mechanical clock. In the case of a pendulum clock, the escapement delivers the regular pushes that keep the pendulum swinging. An escapement also regulates the energy that keeps the clock going. It is the design of the escapement that controls *when* the gears push on the pendulum and *how hard* the gears push.

How does an escapement work? An essential part of the mechanism is the toothed wheel, or driving wheel, which is turned by a string attached to a heavy weight. As the pendulum swings back and forth, the wheel "escapes" for just a moment, allowing it to turn just one tooth at a time. The moving wheel gives the pendulum enough of a push to keep it swinging. Figure 13-1 shows what the escapement mechanism looks like in a real clock.

Figure 13-1

The escapement mechanism for a grandfather clock

Students will be working with an escapement mechanism over the next three lessons. Today they will assemble it. Figure 13-2 shows a detailed picture of the student-built escapement mechanism and a description of how it works. Although the illustration may give the impression that the device moves slowly, actually all four steps occur within seconds. (Student instructions at the end of the lesson, pg. 130, and in the Student Activity Book, pg. 55, explain how to assemble the escapement.)

Working with the escapement mechanism will provide students with a practical technological challenge. Students will strive to resolve these challenges by doing the following:

■ Understanding the function of the device.

■ Troubleshooting its operation.

■ Modifying its characteristics to make it run for as long as possible.

Materials

For each student
   1   science notebook

For every two students
   1   end cap, 3.8 cm (1½″) diameter
   1   base
   1   wooden dowel, 1 cm × 60 cm (⅜″ × 24″)
   1   jumbo paper clip
   1   string, 1.5 m (5 ft) long
   1   12-cm (4¾″) rod
   2   18-cm (7⅛″) rods
   2   14-cm (5⅝″) rods
   2   4.5-cm (1¾″) posts
   3   wheels, 5 cm (2″) diameter
   3   bushings, 3.8 cm (1½″) diameter

3 clothespins

4 bearings, 5 × 3.8 cm (2″ × 1½″)

5 7.5-cm (3″) rods

2 large washers, 4 cm (1½″) diameter

1 C-clamp, 7.5 cm (3″)

1 plastic bottle with lid, 500 ml (16 oz)

1 plastic bag

1 copy of **Blackline Master: Some of the Materials for Constructing the Escapement Mechanism**

For the class

1 roll of masking tape

1 copy of the **Blackline Masters: A Grandfather Clock and an Escapement Mechanism**

Preparation

1. Decide how you want to distribute the materials. Figure 13-3 shows one method. Or, you can put the necessary parts in bags and distribute one bag to each group.

2. Duplicate the blackline master on pg. 133. It shows the components of the escapement mechanism at actual size. The drawings will help students distinguish one part from another.

3. The escapements that students assemble in this lesson will be used in the next two lessons. Provide a space to store the assembled devices.

4. Cut one piece of string for each pair of students. Or, have students use the string and paper clips that they used in Lessons 10 through 12.

5. Make a copy of the grandfather clock and escapement drawings from the blackline masters in **Appendix C** (pg. 165). Tape them together to make a display for the classroom.

6. Follow the instructions on pg. 130 to assemble and troubleshoot your own escapement.

   Note: To wind the string and raise the weight, turn the toothed wheel clockwise.

Figure 13-2

How the Escapement Works

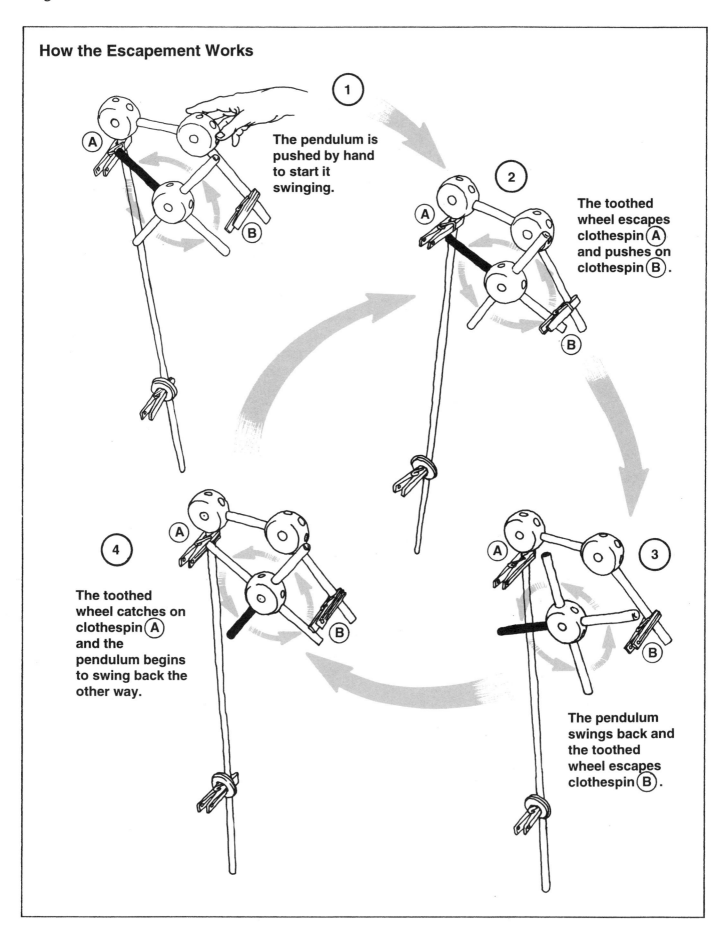

1

The pendulum is pushed by hand to start it swinging.

2

The toothed wheel escapes clothespin (A) and pushes on clothespin (B).

3

The pendulum swings back and the toothed wheel escapes clothespin (B).

4

The toothed wheel catches on clothespin (A) and the pendulum begins to swing back the other way.

Figure 13-3

Distributing the materials

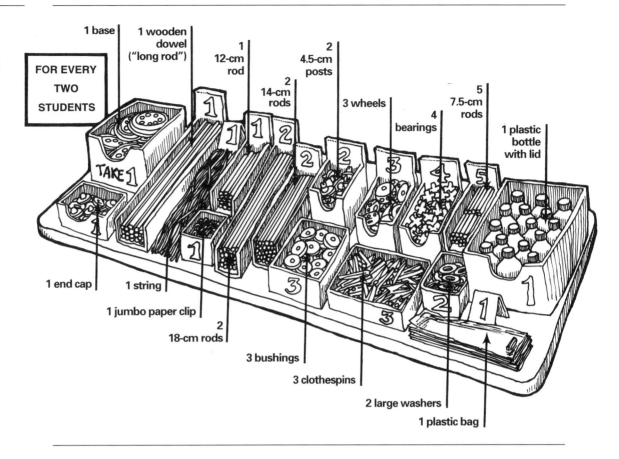

FOR EVERY TWO STUDENTS

1 base
1 wooden dowel ("long rod")
1 12-cm rod
2 14-cm rods
2 4.5-cm posts
3 wheels
4 bearings
5 7.5-cm rods
1 plastic bottle with lid
1 end cap
1 string
1 jumbo paper clip
2 18-cm rods
3 bushings
3 clothespins
2 large washers
1 plastic bag

Procedure

1. Ask students to share the current status of their moon observations. Remind them to continue posting their observations.

2. Remind students that, as they have discussed, using the sun and the moon to keep track of the passage of time has certain disadvantages. Review some of the disadvantages students have identified in earlier lessons.

3. Ask students how they could use a pendulum to keep track of long periods of time—such as a day or the time between full moons. Students' responses probably will include some of the following:

   ■ Count the swings.

   ■ Make a really long pendulum that swings very slowly.

   ■ Use a pendulum clock with gears.

   ■ Take turns staying up all night to keep a pendulum swinging.

4. Explain to students that one solution to the problems of keeping a pendulum swinging and counting the number of swings is a device called an escapement. Then display the large grandfather clock and the clock escapement drawings for students.

5. Ask students to describe similar clocks they have seen. Questions such as the following will help students focus on how the grandfather clock escapement is similar to the student-built escapement.

   ■ Which part of the clock is the pendulum?

   ■ What do you think the clock's hanging weights are used for?

   ■ How do you think the gears are used?

6. Tell students that in the next three lessons they will be working with a pendulum clock escapement. In this lesson, they will follow the plan in the Student Activity Book to assemble the escapement. Over the next two lessons, students will work on making it operate by itself and on using it to measure time.

7. Ask students to use the plan on pg. 55 in the Student Activity Book to help them assemble the escapement. The plan also is included on pg. 130 of the Teacher's Guide.

8. Distribute the materials to students. Ask them to work with a partner to assemble the escapement and investigate its operation.

9. After students have completed assembling the escapement and have had an opportunity to examine it, ask them to put their names on their devices with masking tape and move them to a storage area.

Final Activities

1. Have students write a brief description in their notebooks about how they think the escapement works. Encourage them to include drawings with their descriptions.

2. Ask the class to share their ideas about how the escapement works. Explain that in the next lesson, they will work on getting each device to run by itself.

Extensions

1. Brainstorm with students examples of technologies other than timekeeping that have improved over the years. For instance, lighting devices, motion picture equipment, and calculators have all changed substantially.

2. Survey the class about how they wake up each morning. How many use a device such as a rooster, a clock radio, an alarm clock, or other means? Use a computer graphing program to create a class graph showing the percentage using each method.

Assessment

This lesson is the first of three in which students construct a clock escapement, improve the device they construct, and investigate ways to make it run for as long as possible. The skills that students develop through these activities are somewhat different from those developed earlier. They include the following:

- The ability to follow an assembly plan

- The ability to solve practical problems by **troubleshooting**—changing one thing at a time

- The ability to apply what they have learned to modify and improve a technological device

Performance can be assessed by observing the degree to which students are organized, follow a method, communicate effectively with each other, and make progress toward their goal. In addition, their notebook entries made at the end of this lesson can be compared with similar entries made at the end of the unit to assess the progress students have made in understanding the operation of an escapement.

Figure 13-4

Completed
escapement
mechanism

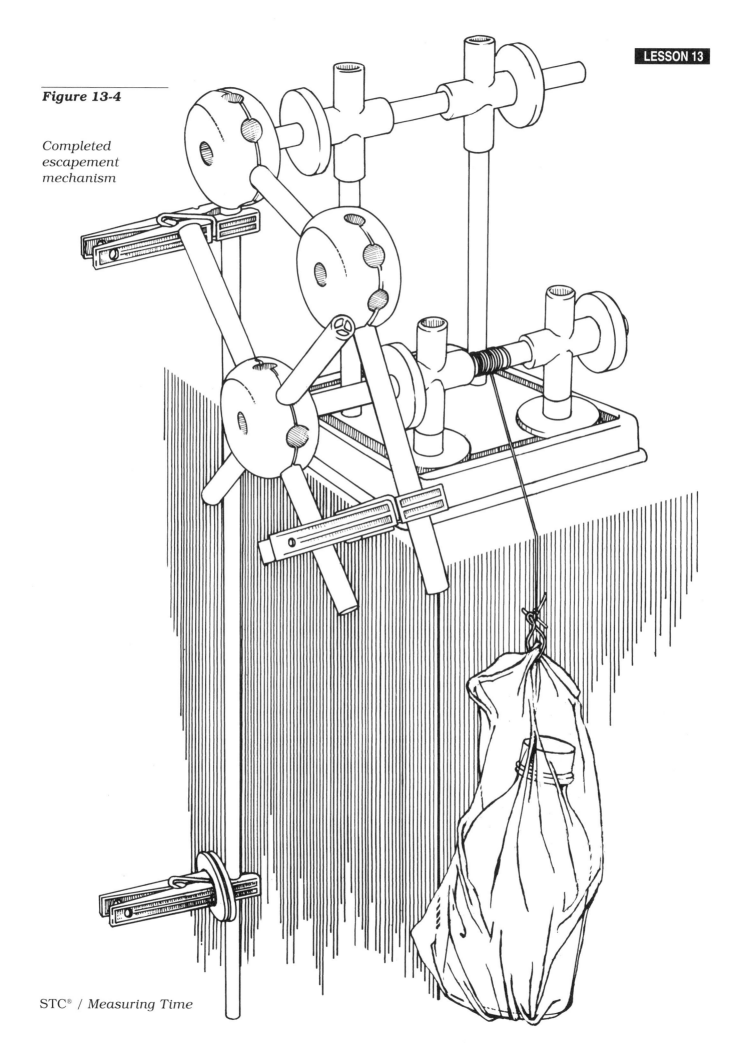

Student Instructions for Assembling the Escapement

1. Put two 14-cm (5⅝-in) rods and two posts in the base.

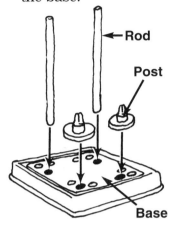

←Rod

Post

Base

2. Put one bearing on top of each of the rods and posts.

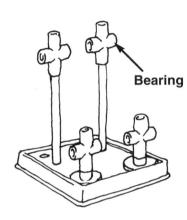

Bearing

3. Put the 18-cm (7⅛-in) rods through the bearings. Wiggle them so that the rods rotate freely.

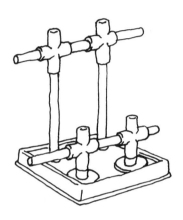

4. Use the bushings to keep the 18-cm (7⅛-in) rods inside the bearings.

Bushings
End Cap

5. Put one of the wheels on the end of the upper 18-cm (7⅛-in) rod. Attach the long wooden dowel to the bottom of this wheel. This is the **pendulum.**

Wheel

Long rod

6. Attach one clothespin and two washers near the bottom of the wooden rod to make the pendulum bob. Check to see that the pendulum swings back and forth freely.

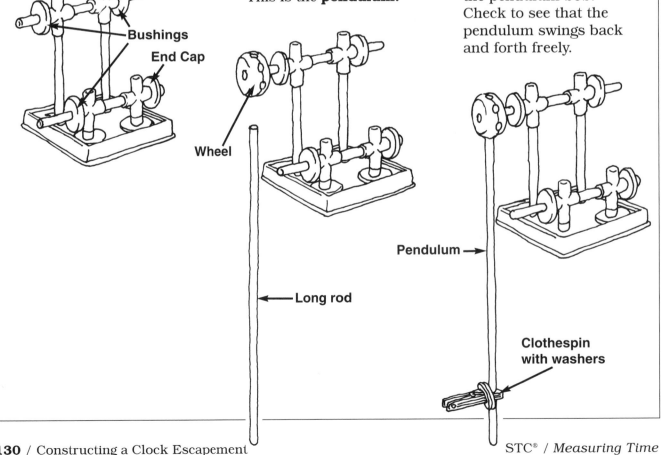

Pendulum →

Clothespin
with washers

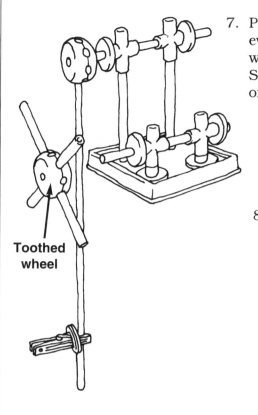

Toothed wheel

7. Place four short 7.5-cm (3-in) rods evenly around another one of the wheels. This is the **toothed wheel.** Slide the toothed wheel onto the end of the lower 18-cm (7⅛-in) rod.

8. Use a small piece of tape to attach the string to the center of the lower 18-cm (7⅛-in) rod. Wind the string around the 18-cm (7⅛-in) rod and hang a bottle of water in a plastic bag on the end of the string. This weight will make the toothed wheel spin rapidly as the string unwinds.

Pallet arm

7.5-cm (3-in) rod

Wheel

12-cm (4¾-in) rod

Pendulum

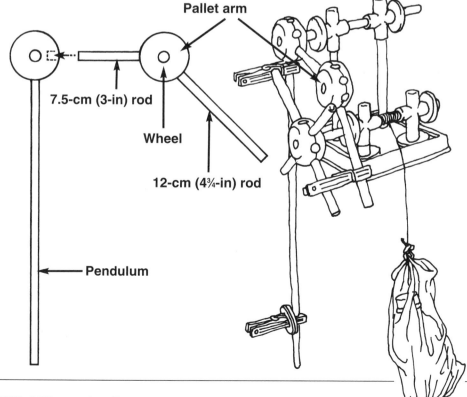

9. Connect the remaining 7.5-cm (3-in) rod and the 12-cm (4¾-in) rod with the remaining wheel. This is called the **pallet arm.**

Attach the pallet arm to the pendulum. The pallet arm will make the toothed wheel push on the pendulum. It also will keep the string from unwinding too quickly.

10. Position the mechanism at the edge of a table or desk so that the weights can fall freely. Use the C-clamp (or heavy tape) to hold the base in place. Then clip one clothespin high on the pendulum and another clothespin onto the pallet arm. Try to place them so that they keep the toothed wheel from unwinding freely.

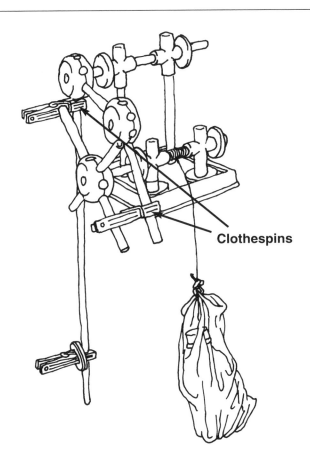

Clothespins

11. Swing the pendulum back and forth so that the toothed wheel catches and pushes on the clothespins one at a time as the wheel turns.

Troubleshooting

Since the pieces will not fit together in exactly the same way every time, you probably will need to make some adjustments to your escapement to get it to work the way you want it to. If you have difficulty, keep trying.

Be patient and adjust one thing at a time. You will get your escapement to operate. This kind of problem solving is called **troubleshooting.** In the next lesson, you will have a chance to troubleshoot your escapement.

Some of the Materials for Constructing the Escapement Mechanism

These materials are shown at actual size.

18-cm (7⅛″) rod

14-cm (5⅝″) rod

12-cm (4¾″) rod

7.5-cm (3″) rod

Wheel

Bushing

Post

Bearing

End Cap

Adjusting the Clock Escapement

Overview and Objectives

In this lesson, students gain a better understanding of how a pendulum clock works by troubleshooting the escapement mechanism they have assembled. They learn to solve a practical problem by manipulating the escapement and applying what they know about its operation to make the device work. These activities prepare students to modify and improve the escapement in Lesson 15.

■ Students brainstorm how to improve the operation of a clock escapement.

■ Students apply practical problem-solving skills to figure out how to make the clock escapement work.

■ Students discuss the results of their troubleshooting strategies.

Background

Practical problem solving is a challenging process. Sometimes called **troubleshooting**, this technique is used to find and correct the causes of problems by changing one thing at a time and learning what effect each change has on the operation of a device or system.

In this lesson, students are asked to solve the practical problem of making a clock escapement work. They will face many different challenges and will consider a variety of ways to overcome them. Some students will need more suggestions and encouragement than others. To keep students from getting frustrated, it may be helpful to have them discuss what they are doing as they work. The exchange of information among groups is a positive way to discourage destructive competition and ensure that all groups are successful.

Materials

For each student
   1   science notebook

For every two students
   1   clock escapement (from Lesson 13)

For the class
   1   clock with a sweep second hand
       Several sheets of newsprint and marker(s)

Preparation

Decide how you will distribute the assembled escapements.

Procedure

1. Ask students for suggestions of things they might try if they have trouble getting their escapements to run. Begin a class list by writing students' ideas on a sheet of newsprint. Their suggestions probably will include some of the troubleshooting tips listed below. Students can list additional ideas after they have had more experience with practical problem solving.

    Troubleshooting Tips
    - Ask another student for suggestions.
    - Change one thing at a time.
    - Put the clock on the corner of the desk, wind the string up the other way, and try again.
    - Check whether the rods are pushed in all the way.
    - Add more weight to make the toothed wheel push harder on the pendulum.
    - Look for ways to make the pendulum swing back and forth freely.
    - Change the position of the clothespins.

2. Challenge students to work with their partners to make their escapements run. If they have trouble, remind them to try the troubleshooting suggestions one at a time.

3. Distribute the clock escapements to students.

4. After students get the escapement working, have them use the two techniques listed below to measure how long it runs.

    - Count the number of times the pendulum swings back and forth without stopping.
    - Use the wall clock to measure how many seconds the escapement runs.

    This activity will help students focus both on the frequency of the pendulum and on the push of the driving weight. These factors affect the escapement's operation. Then remind students to record their measurements in their notebooks.

Final Activities

1. Ask students to share with the class some of the steps they took to solve the problem of getting the escapement to work. Add their new ideas to the class chart.

2. Have each group report on the number of swings their pendulum makes without stopping. Remind them that their goal in the next lesson is to make the escapement run even longer—for as long as possible.

Extensions

1. Ask students to examine carefully the mechanical workings of a wind-up toy. The mechanical motors on most such toys use a spring-driven escapement mechanism, not a pendulum.

2. Challenge students to estimate how many times they would have to wind their clocks to measure the length of one day. Ask them how many times they would have to wind it to measure one month and one year.

Figure 14-1

*Troubleshooting
the operation
of the clock
escapement*

Assessment

Below are some areas to observe as you assess your students' work with
their escapements:

- Use the number of swings without stopping, recorded in students'
  notebooks, as a baseline for assessing their progress in Lesson 15.

- Determine whether students are able to improve the operation of their
  escapement. Are they able to make it run for a longer period of time?
  Have they developed their ability to troubleshoot?

- Take note of how well students communicate with others about what
  they are doing. Are they able to work as a team with their partners?

Calibrating the Clock

Overview and Objectives

Using what they have learned in previous lessons, students strive to overcome the problem of creating a clock that will run for a longer period of time. Their challenge is to make the longest-running clock escapement that they can. This activity provides students with an opportunity to practice their ability to manipulate a mechanical device and to apply what they have learned about how it works.

■ Students identify variables that affect the length of time that the clock escapement will operate.

■ Students engage in a practical challenge to invent ways to maximize the running time of the clock escapement.

Background

In the last lesson, students manipulated the parts of the escapement in order to make it operate. In this lesson, they identify the variables that may have an effect on how long it will operate. These include the following:

■ The length of the pendulum (position of the bob)

■ The amount of weight used to turn the toothed wheel

■ The weight of the pendulum bob

■ The length of the string used to turn the toothed wheel

The students' challenge is to increase the running time. The most straight-forward way to do this is to lengthen the string and to increase the height from which the driving weight falls. There are practical limits to how high the clock can be; some students may devise methods to extend the distance the weight falls by looping the string up and over something.

Another way to increase the running time is to decrease the frequency of the pendulum. Students learned in Lessons 10 through 12 that lengthening a pendulum makes it swing back and forth less frequently. Moving the washers down the rod has the effect of lengthening the pendulum. This is a more challenging method for increasing the running time because other adjustments will be necessary, such as moving the clothespins.

Materials

For each student

1   science notebook

For every two students

1   assembled escapement
1   calculator (if available)

For the class

1   clock with a sweep second hand
1   class list of students' ideas for making the escapement work ("Troubleshooting Tips," from Lesson 14)
    Several sheets of newsprint and marker(s)

Preparation

1. Display the class list of troubleshooting ideas from Lesson 14.

2. Prepare a sheet of newsprint with the heading "Variables that May Affect How Long the Escapement Will Run."

Procedure

1. Ask students to share how they made a clock escapement in Lesson 13.

2. Ask students to help make a class list of variables that may affect how long the escapement will run. The list will probably include some of the variables addressed in the troubleshooting tips from Step 1 of the **Procedure** section in Lesson 14 (pg. 136).

3. Explain to students that their challenge is to increase the length of time that their escapement operates by changing one or more of the variables they have identified. Then have students find the running time that they recorded in their notebooks in Lesson 14 and identify that as the "time to beat."

4. Ask students to keep a careful record in their notebooks of the changes they make to their escapement devices and the effect these changes have on the running time. Ask them to record changes that reduce the running time as well as those that increase it. Figure 15-1 shows a sample notebook entry.

    Note: Making changes to the escapement may cause it to stop working the way it did previously. In a complex device such as an escapement, it is often difficult to change one variable without having an immediate effect on others. If the escapement stops working, encourage students to troubleshoot until it starts working again.

5. Distribute the escapements to students and ask them to begin work.

6. After students have had adequate time to experiment with lengthening the running time of the escapements, ask them to return the materials to the storage area.

Final Activities

1. Ask students to use calculators (if available) to determine the change in the running time of their escapements from Lessons 14 to 15. Encourage them to use several methods to measure the change. An example is included below.

    ■   *The number of seconds.* Ask students to find the increase or decrease in the running time by subtracting the smaller number from the larger. For example, if the Lesson 14 time was 45 seconds and the longest running time in Lesson 15 was 125 seconds, then the increase was 80 seconds, or 1 minute and 20 seconds.

Figure 15-1

*Sample
notebook page*

What we changed	Result
First we tried putting the washers near the top	The pendulum swung faster than before and the clock ran for 35 seconds.
We changed the clothpins because they weren't hitting the gears right.	It works again now
Next, we put the clock on some books.	It ran for 40 seconds before the weight hit the floor.
Tried putting the washers halfway down.	Didn't work
Moved the clothespin back	It ran for 1 min and 20 secs.

- *The percentage change.* Ask students to calculate the percentage increase (or decrease) in the running time. Using the above example, the percentage increase was

$$\frac{125 - 45}{45} \times 100 = 177\%$$

- *The improvement ratio.* Ask students to compute the ratio of the improved time to the Lesson 14 time. In the above example, the improvement ratio was

$$\frac{125}{45} = 2.8, \text{ or almost three times as long}$$

2. Ask students to calibrate the escapements by comparing them with a wall clock. Have students mark how much time the escapements will measure at various key points. For example, suggest that they mark how much time it takes for the string to unwind halfway.

3. Ask students to report briefly on the improvements they have made to their escapements. Remind them to include both the changes they made to their escapements and the results of those changes.

Extensions

1. Challenge students to make their escapements appear more clocklike, perhaps by adding a dial and a hand on the opposite end of the toothed wheel. Figure 15-2 shows what this might look like.

Figure 15-2

A clock face and a hand added to the escapement

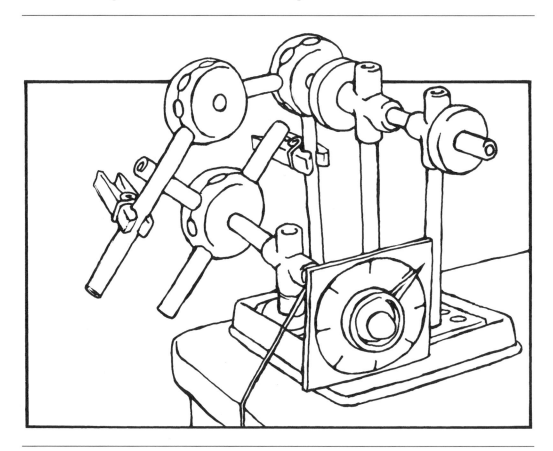

2. Ask students to design and construct a clock escapement using materials from home. *Clocks*, by Bernie Zubrowski (see **Bibliography, Appendix B**), contains a number of useful models for students.

Assessment

1. Look for improvements that students have made in their troubleshooting ability. Are they able to solve problems by themselves, or do they require repeated prompting?

2. Examine students' notebooks for evidence that they have improved the operation of the escapement. Have students described the effects of changing some of the variables they identified? Have students succeeded in increasing the length of time that the device runs?

Building a One-Minute Timer

Overview and Objectives

In this culminating lesson, students apply what they have learned about timekeeping devices to the problem of estimating the duration of a one-minute interval. Students first encountered this problem in Lesson 1. Today students are asked to design and construct a device that can be used to signal the passing of one minute. This lesson is an embedded assessment. It provides you with information on how students are able to apply what they have learned about timekeeping devices.

- Students use the records in their notebooks to help them plan a one-minute timer.

- Students construct a device to measure a one-minute interval of time.

Background

Students will approach this lesson in a variety of ways. If few limits are placed on the task, a great number of materials will be required. Additional or substitute materials could be provided to increase the diversity of students' responses to the "build a timer" challenge (be sure to plan the classroom management of these new materials). Some suggestions for additional materials are listed below.

Small paper cups	Plastic soda bottles
Sand	Marbles
Long rubber bands (for a "spring pendulum")	Cardboard tubes

This lesson can be easily extended to permit students to develop a timer as an at-home project. In this case, it may be necessary to provide students with time to plan their projects on a separate day before they build their timekeeping devices.

Materials

For each student
  1   science notebook

For the class
  1   clock with a sweep second hand
      Sinking water clocks (Lessons 7, 8, 9)
      Pendulums (Lessons 10, 11, 12)
      Escapements (Lessons 13, 14, 15)

Preparation

1. Decide what materials you will provide for students. The **Background** section contains suggestions for additional materials that students might find useful. If several groups used their pendulum strings in their escapements, you may need to prepare more lengths of string.

    Management Tip: If you are planning to have students collect additional materials for this activity, it will be necessary to conduct Steps 1, 2, and 3 of the **Procedure** section at least one day before building the devices.

2. Display a clock with a sweep second hand in the classroom.

Procedure

1. Ask students to describe the various devices they have investigated. Ask students to suggest some ways to use these devices to keep track of the passage of a minute. Make a class list of their ideas. Their suggestions are likely to include some of the following:

    ■ Adjust the escapement so that it unwinds in one minute.

    ■ Make a pendulum the right length so that it swings once each second. Then count 60 swings.

    ■ Build an aluminum foil boat that sinks in one minute.

    ■ Use a long pendulum and count the number of swings it makes in one minute.

    ■ Build a sinking clock that has a very small hole in it. Add weight until the clock sinks in exactly one minute.

    Note: Some students may suggest using the materials to build one-minute timers that are different from the devices that students have investigated. For example, one student who worked on this activity suggested making a "dripping clock" that measured time by keeping track of how long it took for water to drip out of a partially clogged funnel.

2. Suggest that students review their notebook entries from previous lessons for clues about how to design a one-minute timer. Encourage students to discuss their ideas with each other.

3. Ask students to write plans for their timers in their notebooks. Have them include a drawing, a list of materials, and an explanation of how the timer can be used to keep track of the length of a minute.

4. Challenge students to build the timers they have planned. Remind them to use their plans and to ask for suggestions from other students to help them with their timers.

5. Distribute the materials to students. Ask those students who are working with water to share water tanks.

Figure 16-1

Building a
one-minute timer

Final Activities

1. Ask students to compare their devices by using them to gauge the length of a minute. Position the wall clock so that you are the only person who can see it. Then ask students to signal the end of a one-minute interval after you signal the beginning of the interval.

2. Discuss with students their ideas about why all the estimated minutes did not end at the same time. Questions such as the following may help focus the discussion on the need for standard measures of time:

   ■ What are some reasons that your estimate of a minute is different from other students' estimates?

   ■ How could we agree on the length of a minute?

Extensions

1. Encourage students to continue refining their timers so that they can estimate one minute more accurately. Ask them to keep a record of the changes they make.

2. Ask students to use their timers to compare the length of time it takes to do some of the following:

   ■ Play the "Minute Waltz."

   ■ Fry a minute steak.

   ■ Cook a three-minute egg.

   ■ Make a five-minute telephone call.

3. Challenge students to design their own "clock faces" or other scales so that the timekeeping devices they have created also can measure quarter- and half-minutes.

Assessment

This final lesson is a natural place to assess the progress students have made. As mentioned in the **Overview and Objectives** section, this lesson serves as an embedded assessment because it provides you with information not only about students' ability to plan and construct a one-minute timer but also about how well they understand timekeeping devices in general. In particular, look for evidence that students can do the following:

   ■ Develop a workable plan and follow it. Do the plans they wrote in their notebooks match the devices they constructed?

   ■ Adjust the length of time that the devices measure. Can students manipulate one variable at a time to alter the timer in a predictable way?

   ■ Understand how their timers operate.

Post-Unit Assessment

The post-unit assessment on pg. 149 is a matched follow-up to the pre-unit assessment in Lesson 1. By comparing students' pre- and post-unit responses, you will be able to document their growth in understanding both the history of timekeeping and the different types of timekeeping devices.

Final Assessments

Final assessments for this unit are provided in **Appendix A,** on pg. 151. They include a self-assessment for students and assessments on applying information about different timekeeping devices.

Post-Unit Assessment

Overview

This post-unit assessment of students' ideas about time is matched to the pre-unit assessment in Lesson 1. By comparing the individual and class responses from Lesson 1 with the responses from these activities, you will be able to document students' learning over the course of the unit. During the first brainstorming session, students developed two lists—"What We Know about Measuring Time" and "Questions We Have about Measuring Time." They also thought about how they would tell time if they did not have a clock or watch. When they revisit these activities during the assessment, students are likely to appreciate how much they have learned about the history of timekeeping and about the devices used to measure time.

Materials

For each student

  1 science notebook

For the class

    Class lists from Lesson 1

Procedure

1. Ask students to reconsider the question of how they would tell time without a clock or watch. Have them record their ideas in their science notebooks. When you compare students' journal entries from Lesson 1 with their entries in this matched post-unit assessment, look for both refinement of ideas and evidence given in support of ideas.

2. Ask students to think about their work during the unit. What do they now know about measuring time? What questions do they now have? Have them write their thoughts in their notebooks.

3. Display the class lists from Lesson 1. Ask students to identify statements on the lists that they now know to be true. What experiences did they have during the unit that confirmed these statements?

4. Ask students to identify statements they would like to correct or improve. What is their evidence?

5. Ask students to contribute new information to the lists. What else have they learned? What new questions do they have?

Final Assessments

Overview

Following are some suggestions for assessment activities. Although it is not essential to do all these activities, it is recommended that students do Assessment 1.

■ Assessment 1 is a student self-assessment.

■ Assessment 2 is a series of questions about sun clocks, sinking water clocks, and pendulums.

■ Assessment 3 asks students to make new predictions about the moon's phases on the basis of the observations they have made during the unit.

Assessment 1

Student Self-Assessment

Using a questionnaire, students assess their own learning and participation during the unit.

Materials

For each student

1 Student Self-Assessment (on pg. 152)

Procedure

1. Discuss the Student Self-Assessment with the class. Explain to the students that it is important to stop from time to time and think about how they are working.

2. Allow students sufficient time to complete the self-assessment either in class or as a homework assignment.

Measuring Time:
Student Self-Assessment

Name: _____

Date: _____

1. What do you now know about measuring time without clocks that you did not know before?

2. What do you now know about clocks that you did not know before?

3. How well do you think you and your partner(s) worked together? Give some examples.

4. What did you learn from planning and conducting your own experiments? Give some examples of your experiments.

5. Identify activities in the unit you enjoyed. Explain why you liked them.

6. Were there any activities in the unit you did not understand or that confused you? Explain your answer.

7. Take another look at your record sheets, graphs, and science notebook. Describe how well you think you recorded your observations and ideas.

8. How do you feel about science?

Assessment 2	**Questions about Clocks**

Materials

For each student
1   science notebook
1   copy of **Blackline Master: Questions about Clocks**

Procedure

Ask students to respond orally or in writing and drawing to the questions on their copy of the blackline master, which has spaces for students to write their responses. Look for evidence in their responses that they have begun to make sense for themselves of the phenomena that they have experienced in the unit. You may want to encourage students to use their notebooks for this activity to help them remember what they have done in past lessons.

1. A sun shadow clock, like the one you made in Lesson 3, casts a shadow as shown in the drawing.

    ■ What time of day do you think it is according to the clock?

Figure A-1

Sun clock

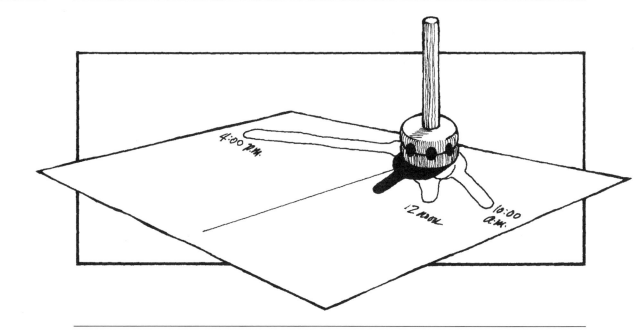

■ What are your reasons for thinking that?

■ Draw in four additional shadows. Label each one with the time of day that you think it will occur.

2. This data table was completed while doing an experiment with a sinking water clock. Use the blank grid to label and construct a graph of the data. Explain what the graph shows.

Sample data table and graph grid

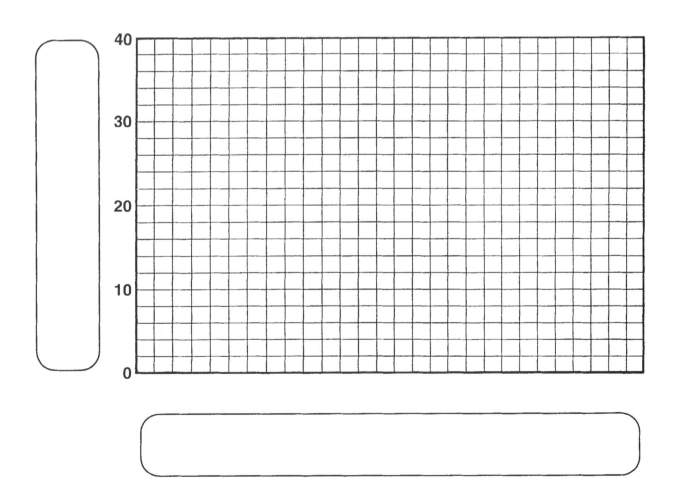

Investigating Sinking Water Clocks

Number of Washers	Size of the Hole (Color of the Bead)	Number of Seconds until Sunk
1	yellow	37 seconds
2	yellow	14 seconds
3	yellow	10 seconds
4	yellow	9 seconds

3. In Lesson 11, you conducted an experiment on pendulums. The graph below shows the data that one group of students collected while conducting a similar experiment.

Figure A-3

Sample graph

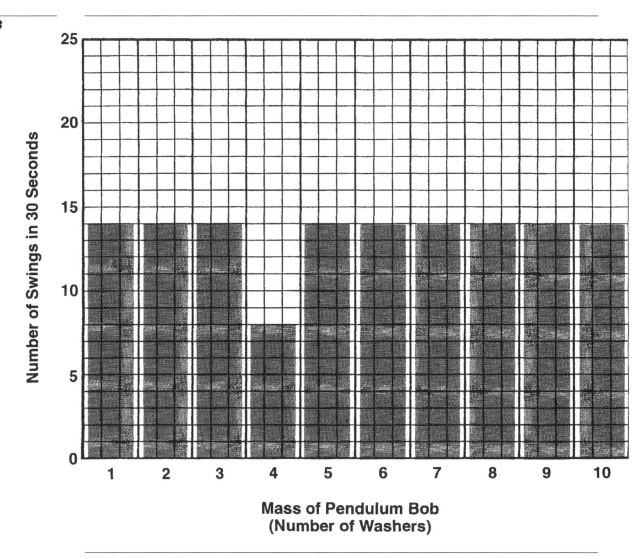

- Look at the graph. What was the frequency of the pendulum when the weight of the pendulum bob was seven washers?

- Now look on the graph for the pendulum's frequency when the weight of the pendulum bob was four washers. What are two possible ways to explain why this frequency is so different from the others?

Explanation 1:

Explanation 2:

Assessment 3   **Reviewing Moon Predictions**

Materials   *For each student*
    1 science notebook
    1 strip of adding machine paper, 450 cm (18″)

Procedure

1. Ask students to draw on the strips of paper their predictions about how the moon will appear during the next 14 days if no clouds are in the sky. Encourage them to use their observation strips from the unit as a guide. Ask them to explain the reasons for their predictions on the back of the strips of paper.

   Look for evidence that these new predictions are based on the observations they have made of the moon's changing appearance over time. Use these predictions to encourage students to continue their moon observations.

2. Ask students to write and draw in their notebooks in response to the following question:

   ■ What do you think causes the moon's phases?

   Look for evidence that students' understanding of the complex causes of the moon's phases has increased.

Bibliography

The **Bibliography** is divided into the following categories:

- Resources for Teachers
- Resources for Students
- Additional Resources: Time Travel

While not a complete list of the many books written on the history of timekeeping and timekeeping devices, this bibliography is a sampling of books that complement this unit. These materials come well recommended. They have been favorably reviewed, and teachers have found them useful.

If a book goes out of print or if you seek additional titles, you may wish to consult the following resources.

Appraisal: Science Books for Young People (The Children's Science Book Review Committee, Boston, MA).

> Published quarterly, this periodical reviews new science books available for young people. Each book is reviewed by a librarian and by a scientist. The Children's Science Book Review Committee is sponsored by the Science Education Department of Boston University's School of Education and the New England Roundtable of Children's Librarians.

National Science Resources Center. *Science for Children: Resources for Teachers.* Washington, DC: National Academy Press, 1988.

> This volume provides a wealth of information about resources for hands-on science programs. It describes science curriculum materials, supplementary materials (science activity books, books on teaching science, reference books, and magazines), museum programs, and elementary science curriculum projects.

Science and Children (National Science Teachers Association, Washington, DC).

> Each March, this monthly periodical provides an annotated bibliography of outstanding children's science trade books primarily for pre-kindergarten through eighth-grade science teachers.

Science Books & Films (American Association for the Advancement of Science, Washington, DC).

Published nine times a year, this periodical offers critical reviews of a wide range of new science materials, from books to audiovisual materials to electronic resources. The reviews are primarily written by scientists and science educators. *Science Books & Films* is useful for librarians, media specialists, curriculum supervisors, science teachers, and others responsible for recommending and purchasing scientific materials.

Scientific American (Scientific American, Inc., New York).

Each December, Philip and Phylis Morrison compile and review a selection of outstanding new science books for children.

Sosa, Maria, and Shirley M. Malcom, eds. *Science Books & Films: Best Books for Children, 1988-91.* Washington, DC: American Association for the Advancement of Science Press, 1992.

This volume, part of a continuing series, is a compilation of the most highly rated science books that have been reviewed recently in the periodical *Science Books & Films.*

Resources for Teachers

Aveni, Anthony. *Empires of Time: Calendars, Clocks, and Cultures.* New York: Basic Books, Inc., 1989.

This book contains particularly good background on the development of timekeeping, biological clocks, and Mayan calendars.

Boslough, John. "The Enigma of Time." *National Geographic Magazine,* March 1990, 109-32.

This article explores time and its role in our lives.

Carlson, John B. "America's Ancient Skywatchers." *National Geographic Magazine,* March 1990, 76-107.

This article is a good introduction to the astronomy of the Incas, Mayas, Navajos, and Anasazi.

Diagram Group. *Comparisons.* New York: St. Martin's Press, 1980.

This visual guide shows relative lengths of time.

Dishon, Dee, and Pat Wilson O'Leary. *A Guidebook for Cooperative Learning: Techniques for Creating More Effective Schools.* Holmes Beach, FL: Learning Publications, Inc., 1984.

A practical guide for teachers who are embarking on the implementation of cooperative-learning techniques in the classroom.

Johnson, David W., Roger T. Johnson, and Edythe Johnson Holubec. *Circles of Learning: Cooperation in the Classroom.* Alexandria, VA: Association for Supervision and Curriculum Development, 1984.

This excellent book presents the case for cooperative learning in a concise and readable form. It reviews the research, outlines implementation strategies, and answers many questions.

Mohlenbrock, Robert. "Medicine Mountain, Wyoming." *Natural History*, January 1990, 24-27.

> This brief nontechnical article argues the case that medicine wheels were calendars for predicting the changing seasons.

Rice, Paul. *Timesource*. Berkeley, CA: Ten Speed Press, 1989.

> This collection of short articles on historical and cultural aspects of time and timekeeping is fascinating.

Waugh, Albert. *Sundials: Their Theory and Construction*. New York: Dover Publications, Inc., 1973.

> This is an excellent though technical guide to sundial construction. It is a good reference for any students who want to investigate sundials in more detail.

Resources for Students

Adzeman, Robert, and Mablen Jones. *The Great Sundial Cutout Book*. New York: Hawthorne Books, Inc., 1978.

> This book contains directions and patterns for making 15 different sundials from heavy paper.

Anno, Mitsumasa. *Anno's Sundial*. New York: Philomel Books, 1985.

> This delightful pop-up book is full of different kinds of sundials.

Branley, Franklyn. *The Moon Seems to Change*. New York: Thomas Crowell, 1987.

> This easy-to-read book explains why the moon's shape appears to change. It includes directions for a demonstration of the changing phases.

Burns, Marilyn. *This Book Is about Time*. Boston: Little, Brown, and Co., 1978.

> This book is full of interesting stories about the history of timekeeping and suggestions for student projects and activities.

Clark, Ann Nolan. *Sun Journey: A Story of Zuni Pueblo*. Santa Fe, NM: Ancient City Press, 1988.

> This is the story of a grandfather teaching his grandson Zuni traditions, including how to tell Zuni time and keep the Zuni calendar.

Fisher, Leonard Everett. *Pyramid of the Sun, Pyramid of the Moon*. New York: Macmillan Publishing Co., 1988.

> This is a beautifully illustrated story about Toltec and Aztec astronomy and associated religious customs.

Hadley, Eric, and Tessa Hadley. *Legends of the Sun and Moon*. Cambridge, England: Cambridge University Press, 1983.

> This book contains a dozen myths and tales from around the world. It is an excellent source of non-European myths.

Jacobs, Una. *Sun Calendar*. Morristown, NJ: Silver Burdett Company, 1983.

> This is a collection of short articles about seasons, biological clocks, and the sun.

Jenkins, Gerald, and Magdalen Bear. *Sundials and Timedials: A Collection of Working Models to Cut and Glue Together.* Norfolk, England: Tarquin Publications, 1988.

This book contains patterns and directions for making a number of different sundials.

Moeschl, Richard. *Exploring the Sky: 100 Projects for Beginning Astronomers.* Chicago: Chicago Review Press, 1989.

Some of the projects included in this book are making a Mayan calendar, building a working model of Stonehenge, telling directions from the sun, making sundials and water clocks, and keeping track of the sun during the day. It is an excellent resource for student projects.

Monroe, Jean Guard, and Ray Williamson. *They Dance in the Sky: Native American Star Myths.* Boston: Houghton Mifflin Co., 1987.

This book recounts Native American stories about the constellations.

Perl, Lila. *Blue Monday and Friday the Thirteenth: The Stories Behind the Days of the Week.* New York: Clarion Books, 1986.

Each chapter recounts the mythology and legends associated with each day of the week.

Ross, Frank, Jr. *Oracle Bones, Stars, and Wheelbarrows: Ancient Chinese Science and Technology.* Boston: Houghton Mifflin Co., 1982.

This book includes chapters on Chinese astronomy and inventions, such as water clocks.

Zubrowski, Bernie. *Clocks: Building and Experimenting with Timepieces.* New York: Morrow Junior Books, 1988.

This delightful book is full of ideas and plans for making simple clocks: sun and moon clocks, water clocks, sandglasses, and mechanical clocks. All the projects use easily found materials, such as soda bottles, milk cartons, paper cups, and paper plates.

Additional Resources: Time Travel

At some point during their work with the *Measuring Time* unit, students may ask about the possibilities of time travel. While scientists currently believe that it is impossible, time travel is still an interesting subject.

Popular movies, such as *Back to the Future I, II,* and *III,* offer an excellent starting point for discussion of time travel and for reading about why scientists now believe time travel is impossible. (Traveling in time would violate what physicists call the Law of Causality, and, although it is unnecessary for you to use that term with your students, you could talk about what it deals with. For example, if you could travel back in time and warn Lincoln not to go to Ford's Theatre, then Lincoln wouldn't have been in the theater for Booth to kill. And the historical chain of events that followed Lincoln's assassination would not have been able to occur.)

Many fun books have been written about time travel. Encourage your students to read about it. As a starting point, you might recommend the following. All are available in paperback editions.

Alexander, Lloyd. *Time Cat*. New York: Dell Publishers, 1963.

> Some cats have nine lives; Gareth, the cat of this book, can jump around in time nine times. The adventures of Gareth and Jason, his owner and friend, begin in ancient Egypt and end in America.

Apsley, Brenda, ed. *Doctor Who: Journey through Time*. New York: Crescent Books, 1986.

> Dr. Who is an ageless and timeless adventurer able to travel through time and space. This collection of stories and comic strips is based on a BBC-TV series.

Greer, Gery, and Bob Ruddick. *Max and Me and the Time Machine*. New York: Harper and Row, 1983.

> Max and his best friend, Steve, buy a time machine at a garage sale and find themselves transported back to the Middle Ages. Steve becomes a famous knight, and Max is changed into his trusty horse. In the process of trying to get Max out of the horse's body, they rescue a maiden, fight a tournament with an evil knight, and generally shake up medieval society. Also in the series is *Max and Me and the Wild West*.

L'Engle, Madeleine. *The Time Trilogy: A Wrinkle in Time, A Wind in the Door, and A Swiftly Tilting Planet*. New York: Dell, 1986.

> Trying to rescue their physicist father, the Murray children, Meg and Charles Wallace, jump through time and space with the help of three kind witches.

Twain, Mark. *A Connecticut Yankee in King Arthur's Court*. New York: Airmont Publishing Co., 1964.

> John, an engineer by training, is knocked unconscious and wakes up in the court of King Arthur. The story of how he sets about applying Yankee ingenuity to Arthur's realm is a classic.

Blackline Masters

The following pages are the elements needed to construct a poster of a grandfather clock and its internal mechanism. The sketch and instructions below will help you assemble it.

1. Arrange the pages as shown in the picture. (Note that a blank sheet has been added at lower right to complete the rectangle.)

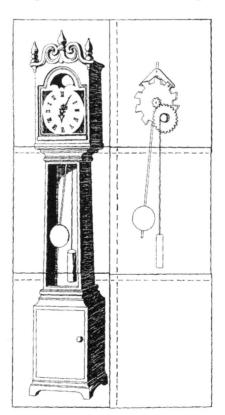

2. Overlap the pages 1½ cm (½″) and tape the pieces together on the back.

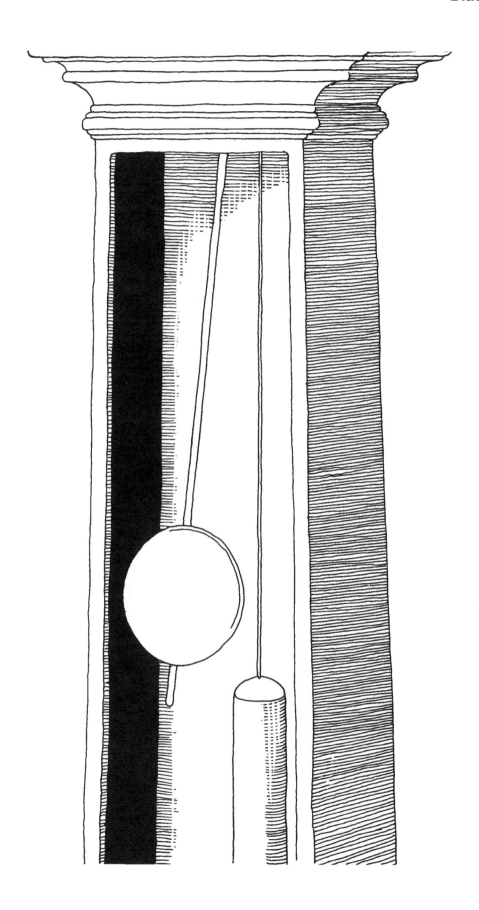

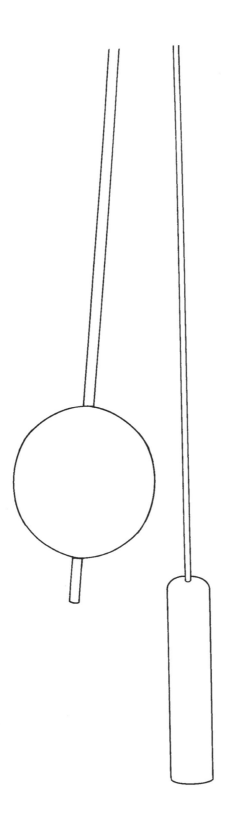

Setting up a Learning Center

Here are a few suggestions of items to include in a learning center for this unit (see also **Appendix F**).

- A world map with time zones indicated
- Trade books on clocks, the sun and moon, the history of timekeeping, time zones, and time travel (see **Bibliography, Appendix B**)
- Articles about current events involving research on time-related topics such as biological clocks, leap seconds, calendars, and atomic clocks
- Materials for additional exploring and experimenting with timekeeping and solar and lunar observation

The following materials will enable students to repeat and extend the experiences they have during the unit:

1 flashlight
1 sundial gnomon
1 set of moon phase cards
1 plastic ball and wood dowel
1 mechanical watch or clock (for disassembly)
1 small sand timer (egg timer)
1 pendulum (3 m of string and a variety of objects to use as pendulum bobs)
2 plastic funnels

Below is a brief explanation of time zones. Your students may find it useful as a companion to the world map in the learning center.

Time Zones

By international agreement, each day begins at the international dateline—an imaginary line drawn from north to south (with some zigs and zags) through the central Pacific Ocean. Since the earth rotates toward the east, sunlight (and therefore daytime) moves westward. Because it takes 24 hours for the earth to rotate once relative to the sun, there are 24 hours in the day. It would seem to follow that there should be 24 evenly spaced time zones around the earth.

However, because time zones conform to political boundaries, there are more than 24 irregularly shaped zones, and the standard times are set by the government of a particular area.

In the United States, the railroad companies played a large role in establishing standard time zones because of their need for a way to maintain predictable rail service according to a schedule. Before standard time zones were established, each city and town set its local time according to the sun. When the sun's position in the sky indicated noontime, the clocks were set to indicate noon.

APPENDIX E

Ancient Observatories

In Lessons 2 and 3, students began to acquire firsthand experience tracking the sun. This appendix provides information about the sky-tracking observatories of early cultures. You may want to use this background information to encourage students to research these remarkable structures on their own.

Stonehenge

Stonehenge, located on the Salisbury Plain about 50 miles west of London, is the most famous of the ancient observatories (Figure E-1). Contrary to popular belief, it was not built by Druids. (Druids were members of the Celtic priesthood living in England, Wales, and Ireland.) Stonehenge was constructed in stages from about 2400 B.C. to 1300 B.C., long before Druids were reported in England.

Stonehenge has always been regarded as an amazing engineering feat, built by humans who used only simple pulleys and levers. In the mid-1960s, an astronomer, Gerald Hawkins, examined the placement of the stones of Stonehenge to see whether they could be used to sight celestial occurrences. He was curious about the fact that from a particular position during the summer solstice, the sun always rises over the same stone—the Heel Stone or Sun Stone. He concluded that Stonehenge was an elaborate astronomical observatory used to mark the changing seasons and predict the occurrence of eclipses.

Hawkins's certainty that Stonehenge was built as an observatory is disputed today. While most astronomers and archaeologists believe that Stonehenge was

Figure E-1

Stonehenge

used as an observatory in some way, they are less certain than Hawkins about why it was built. One theory is that the people who built Stonehenge were sun worshipers who used it as a temple to mark significant points in the sun's apparent journey across the sky.

The Mayan Pyramids

Ancient observatories have been found in other parts of the world, too. The Mayan civilization, which had a well-developed calendrical system, appears to have planned cities along an axis that points to the solstices. The great pyramid at Chichen Itza (pronounced chee-CHEN eet-ZAH), the Pyramid of Kukulcan (pronounced koo-kool-KHAN), is aligned along such lines. In addition, all its steps, including the platform, equal 365, the number of days in the solar year. At equinox, the sun casts shadows down the pyramid that resemble the body of a serpent. The serpent's head, carved in stone, sits at the base of the pyramid; at the equinoxes the head and shadows connect.

Medicine Wheel

Native Americans also built what archaeologists and astronomers believe were observatories. One example is the Medicine Wheel, located on Medicine Mountain in Wyoming's Big Horn National Forest. The wheel is a large, nearly circular arrangement of rocks and stones. From the center, 28 spokes radiate out to the rim. Again, it is not possible to state with certainty that the wheel was constructed only to track the motion of the sun. It may have been constructed for both religious and astronomical purposes, which in many Native American cultures were synonymous. In any event, the alignment of the wheel is such that it can be used to locate the position of the sun at the solstices and equinoxes. It also locates bright stars one month before and one month after the sun's equinox or solstice. Thus, the Medicine Wheel could have been used to predict the changing seasons.

In addition to the observatories mentioned here, there were many other ancient observatories and astronomers. "America's Ancient Skywatchers," an article in the March 1990 issue of *National Geographic Magazine*, describes some of these. Many books, some of which are listed in the **Bibliography**, also contain information about ancient observatories.

The Moon

As mentioned in Lessons 5 and 6, students' understanding of the cause of the moon's phases will evolve through repeated, ongoing observation of the moon. A learning center (see **Appendix D**) can be a valuable resource for students, providing them with information about clocks, the sun, and the moon that is not available from direct observation. Scale models also may help some students visualize the earth, the moon, and the sun from a different perspective.

Resources that could be placed in the learning center include

- Resource information about lunar exploration, such as photographs and descriptions of the Apollo missions and a large map of the moon
- The bead and flashlight used in Lesson 6 to produce moon phases
- Trade books about clocks, the sun, time zones, and the moon
- Articles and pictures describing recent lunar and solar eclipses
- Folklore about the moon
- Books and stories about time travel
- Binoculars for viewing the moon when it is visible during the day
- Information about eclipses (see the explanation and illustrations beginning on pg. 176)

If you provide scale models, remember that they should accurately represent the size of the earth, moon, and sun and the relative distance between them. The table on the following page lists the sizes and average distances between these objects.

If the earth is represented by a marble (12.8 mm in diameter), then the moon would be represented by a BB (3.5 mm in diameter) and located 30 marble diameters (38.4 cm) away. The sun would be an oversized beach ball (1.4 m in diameter) and located 11,400 marble diameters (146 m) away. If your classroom has a window, it may be possible to display a 1.4-m disk outside on the playground (146 m from your classroom).

An alternative model uses an 18-mm-diameter white plastic bead as the moon, and a tennis ball (approx. 66 mm in diameter) as the earth. In this model, the earth and the moon are separated by 30 tennis-ball diameters (approx. 2 m). The sun in this model is an enormous sphere (7.3 m in diameter) located approximately 750 m (almost a half mile) away.

The Relationship Between the Earth, the Moon, and the Sun

Object	Average Diameter (kilometers)	Average Distance from Earth (meters)
Earth	12,750	—
Moon	3,475	384,400
Sun	390,000	145,600,000

Note: The problem with providing a scale model that will fit in the classroom is that the earth and moon need to be extremely small. This may make it difficult for students to visualize what the objects represent.

Eclipses

Discussion of the moon's phases inevitably leads to questions about eclipses. Eclipses of the moon, or **lunar eclipses,** occur when the full moon moves into the earth's shadow. They do not occur with each full moon because the moon is usually a little north or south of the earth's shadow. Lunar eclipses usually take place once or twice a year. But an eclipse is not visible to people everywhere on earth for a variety of reasons, including the fact that they last only a few hours, so people on the "sunny side" of earth during a lunar eclipse do not get to see it. By the time the earth rotates so that they can see the moon, the eclipse is over. Figure F-1(A) shows a lunar eclipse.

In order to simulate a lunar eclipse, use a scale model of the earth and moon as described above and place a light source, such as an overhead projector, at one end of the classroom—as far from the scale model as possible. Maintaining the scaled distance between the earth and moon model may help students understand how the earth's shadow is not cast on the moon during each full moon. A lunar eclipse occurs only when the earth is directly between the moon and sun.

Similarly, solar eclipses occur during a new moon, when the moon is between the earth and sun. They do not occur during each new moon because the moon is not exactly between the earth and sun; it usually is a little north or south of this spot. Figure F-2 shows a solar eclipse.

Figure F-1

Illustration A shows a lunar eclipse. The moon is passing through the earth's shadow. In illustration B, the path of the moon misses the earth's shadow.

A

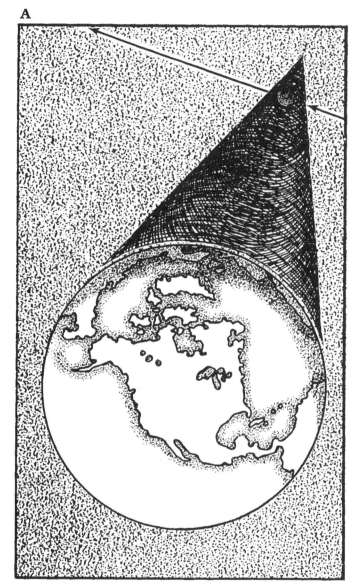

B

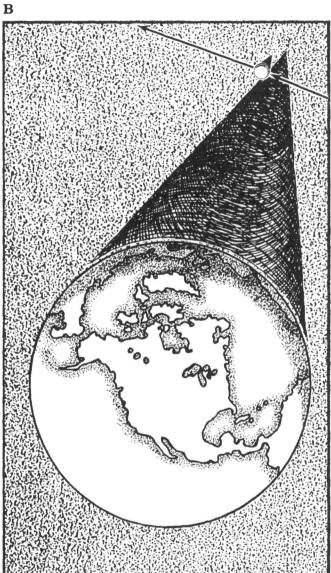

Figure F-2

A solar eclipse occurs whenever the moon casts a shadow on the earth. The eclipse is seen only at those points on the earth that are crossed by the moon's shadow as it moves.

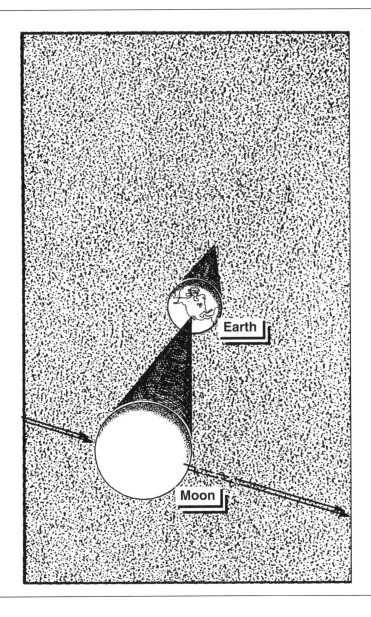

Glossary

Analyze: To study something by breaking it down into simpler parts.

Bob: A weight at the end of a line or rod; for example, the weight at the end of a pendulum.

Calendar: A device or system used to keep track of the passage of time.

Calibrate: To put marks on a scale, container, or other device so that any measurements taken using it will be accurate and consistent.

Cause: Something that produces an effect.

Classify: To group two or more things together because they share one or more properties.

Conclusion: A decision that is based on observations or on a study of data.

Constant: A condition in a controlled experiment that is not changed.

Controlled experiment: A scientific investigation in which one variable is changed and all the others are kept the same, or constant.

Data: Information, such as that gathered during an experiment.

Eclipse: The complete or partial hiding of one body in the sky as it passes into the shadow of another. For example, an eclipse occurs when the moon passes between the sun and the earth, or when the moon enters the shadow of the earth.

Effect: Something brought about by a cause: a result.

Escapement: A mechanism that controls wheel movement and balance in a clock or timepiece.

Experiment: A procedure that is carried out to investigate a scientific question.

Frequency: The number of times a certain process, such as the back-and-forth swing of a pendulum, occurs in a given period of time.

Gnomon: An object that, by the length or position of its shadow, tells the time of day.

Hypothesis: A prediction about how something works or how two variables are related.

Infer: To draw a conclusion about a specific event based on observations and data.

Invent: To think up or create something for the first time.

Metronome: A device that marks precise intervals of time by clicking.

Opinion: An expression of how one feels or thinks about something. An opinion is based on personal views, not necessarily on facts.

Pattern: A repeating arrangement of shapes, colors, numbers, or other things.

Pendulum: A body that is suspended by a string or wire from a fixed point and that can swing back and forth.

Phase: A stage in a process. The apparent shape of the moon at any time is an example of a phase.

Property: Something about an object that helps identify it.

Result: Effect; something produced by a cause.

Troubleshoot: To observe and test a device to see why it is not working.

Variable: An element in an experiment that can be changed.

Weight: A measurement of the force of gravity on an object.

Zenith: The highest point; in astronomy, the point that is directly overhead in the sky.